Close Reading

Grade 7

CARNEGIE
LEARNING

PITTSBURGH, PA

Close Reading, Grade 7

Care has been taken to verify the accuracy of information presented in this book. However, the authors, editors, and publisher cannot accept responsibility for Web, e-mail, newsgroup subject matter or content, or for consequences from application of the information in this book, and make no warranty, expressed or implied, with respect to its content.

Trademarks: Some of the product names and company names included in this book have been used for identification purposes only and may be trademarks or registered trade names of their respective manufacturers and sellers. The authors, editors, and publisher disclaim any affiliation, association, or connection with, or sponsorship or endorsement by, such owners.

ISBN 978-1-53384-163-6

© by Carnegie Learning, Inc.
501 Grant St., Suite 1075
Pittsburgh, PA 15219
E-mail: info@carnegielearning.com
Web site: www.emcschool.com

Printed in the United States of America

27 26 25 24 23 22 21 20   3 4 5 6 7 8 9 10

CONTENTS

= Close Reading Video in Passport

INTRODUCTION TO CLOSE READING

Practicing the close reading process will help you develop the ability to read complex texts independently and proficiently. And you will be able to apply these reading skills to texts across subject areas, such as science or even math, to become a successful reader in all of your classes.

The *Mirrors & Windows* Close Reading Models at the beginning of each unit walk you through applying the close reading process to fiction, nonfiction, poetry, drama, folk literature, and speeches. The *Close Reading* workbook provides students the opportunity to interact with the models by taking notes, marking the text, and completing graphic organizers.

In the Explore section of Passport, Close Reading Videos provide a step-by-step guided demonstration of the Close Reading Process applied directly to the models from your textbook. The selections with accompanying Close Reading Videos are indicated in the Contents with ⬤.

The Close Reading Process

Close reading means to uncover layers of meaning in a text that lead to a deep comprehension. It's an intensive analysis of a text to discover what it says, how it says it, and what it means. Close reading a text involves careful and repeated readings to uncover the layers of meaning.

FIRST READING Key Ideas and Details

During the First Reading you are concerned with *what* the text says. You are asking the questions "What is this about, and how do I know? What can I learn from reading this text? Read to find out what the text is about and what the author's purpose might be for writing it.

SECOND READING Craft and Structure

During the Second Reading you are trying to understand *how* the text says it. You are asking "How do the author's writing style, word choices, and text structure help me understand what he or she is saying?"

THIRD READING Integration of Knowledge and Ideas

And during the Third Reading you go deeper to understand what it *means*. You are asking "What does this text cause me to think or wonder about some larger aspect of the text and the human condition?"

Fiction Close Reading Model

FIRST READING Key Ideas and Details – What the text says

Build Background

You need to apply two types of background to read fiction effectively. One type is the story's literary and historical context. The other type of background is the personal knowledge and experience you bring to your reading.

Set Purpose

A fiction writer presents characters and actions to say something about life. Set your purpose for reading to decide what you want to get out of the story.

Make Connections

Notice where connections can be made between the story and your life or the world outside the story. What feelings or thoughts do you have while reading the story?

Use Reading Skills

Apply skills such as determining author's purpose and using and finding the main idea. Identify a graphic organizer that will help you apply the skill before and while you read.

SECOND READING Craft and Structure – How the text says it

Use Text Organization

Determine the structure of the text and how is it organized.

- Break the text down or "chunk" the text into smaller sections to check your comprehension.
- Stop at the end of paragraphs or sections to summarize what you have read.

Analyze Literature

A fiction writer uses literary techniques, such as plot and setting, to create meaning. What literary elements stand out? Are the characters vivid and interesting? Is there a strong central conflict? As you read, consider how these elements affect your enjoyment and understanding of the story.

Unpack Language

What is the effect of the author's vocabulary and the language choices he or she makes? Make sure to use margin definitions, footnotes, and context clues that give hints to the meaning.

THIRD READING Integration of Knowledge and Ideas – What the text means

Find Meaning

Reread to recall the important details of the story, such as the sequence of events and characters' names. Use this information to interpret, or explain, the meaning of the story.

Make Judgments

Analyze the text by examining details and deciding what they contribute to the meaning. Evaluate the text by making judgments about how the author creates meaning.

Analyze Literature

Review how the use of literary elements increases your understanding of the story. For example, if the author uses dialogue, how does it help to shape the story's meaning?

Extend Understanding

Go beyond the text by applying the story's ideas to your own life and exploring further through writing or other creative projects.

Close Reading

Unit 1

After Twenty Years page 7

SHORT STORY by O. Henry

Build Background

Literary Context O. Henry is best known for his use of the ironic, or surprise, ending. His work has been translated into many languages and has been adapted for movies and television. Since 1919 when it was first given, the O. Henry Award has been one of the most coveted prizes for short story writing.

Reader's Context Can you predict what your friends will be like twenty years from now?

_____

_____

Set Purpose

Skim and scan the story for unfamiliar terms. Also, pay attention to words that are defined in footnotes. Based on these words, try to predict what the story will be about.

Analyze Literature

Plot A **plot** is a series of events related to a central **conflict,** or struggle. A plot usually involves the introduction of the conflict, the events that lead to the **climax**—the point of highest tension in the story—and the **resolution,** the point at which the central conflict is resolved. As you read "After Twenty Years," identify the conflict and make predictions about how the conflict will be resolved.

Use Reading Skills

Analyze Cause and Effect A *cause* is an action or event that results in another event. An *effect* is what happens as the result of an event or action. Analyzing cause-and-effect relationships can help you understand how the events in a story are related. As you read "After Twenty Years," use a chart to keep track of causes and effects.

Cause	Effect
The weather is chilly, rainy, and windy.	The streets are nearly empty.

ha·bit·u·al (hə´ bi ch [ə] wel) *adj.*, behaving in a certain manner by habit

in·tri·cate (in´ tri kət) *adj.*, elaborate

swag·ger (swa´ gər) *n.*, walk with an insolent air; strut

SECOND READ →

Analyze Literature
Plot What do the setting details suggest about possible conflicts in the story?

FIRST READ →

Use Reading Skills
Make Inferences What do these details suggest to you about the man in the doorway?

A Short Story by O. Henry

After Twenty Years

1   The policeman on the beat[1] moved up the avenue impressively. The impressiveness was __habitual__ and not for show, for spectators were few. The time was barely ten o'clock at night, but chilly gusts of wind with a taste of rain in them had well nigh depeopled the streets.

2   Trying doors as he went, twirling his club with many __intricate__ and artful movements, turning now and then to cast his watchful eye down the pacific thoroughfare, the officer, with his stalwart form and slight __swagger,__ made a fine picture of a guardian of the peace. The vicinity was one that kept early hours. Now and then you might see the lights of a cigar store or of an all-night lunch counter, but the majority of the doors belonged to business places that had long since been closed.

3   When about midway of a certain block, the policeman suddenly slowed his walk. In the doorway of a darkened hardware store a man leaned with an unlighted cigar in his mouth. As the policeman walked up to him, the man spoke up quickly.

4   "It's all right, officer," he said reassuringly. "I'm just waiting for a friend. It's an appointment made twenty years ago. Sounds a little funny to you, doesn't it? Well, I'll explain if you'd like to make certain it's all straight. About that long ago there used to be a restaurant where this store stands—'Big Joe' Brady's restaurant."

5   "Until five years ago," said the policeman. "It was torn down then."

6   The man in the doorway struck a match and lit his cigar. The light showed a pale, square-jawed face with keen eyes and a little white scar near his right eyebrow. His scarf pin was a large diamond, oddly set.

7   "Twenty years ago tonight," said the man, "I dined here at 'Big Joe' Brady's with Jimmy Wells, my best chum[3] and the finest chap in the world. He and I were raised here in New York, just like two brothers, together. I was eighteen and Jimmy was twenty. The next morning I was to start for the West to make my fortune. You couldn't have dragged Jimmy out of New York; he thought it was the only place on earth. Well, we

---

1. beat. Area regularly patrolled by a policeman

agreed that night that we would meet here again exactly twenty years from that date and time, no matter what our conditions might be or from what distance we might have to come. We figured that in twenty years each of us ought to have our destiny worked out and our fortunes made, whatever they were going to be."

8 "It sounds pretty interesting," said the policeman. "Rather a long time between meets, though, it seems to me. Haven't you heard from your friend since you left?"

9 "Well, yes, for a time we corresponded,"² said the other. "But after a year or two we lost track of each other. You see, the West is a pretty big proposition, and I kept hustling around over it pretty lively. But I know Jimmy will meet me here if he's alive, for he always was the truest, **staunchest** old chap in the world. He'll never forget. I came a thousand miles to stand in this door tonight, and it's worth it if my old partner turns up⁵."

10 The waiting man pulled out a handsome watch, the lids of it set with small diamonds.

11 "Three minutes to ten," he announced. "It was exactly ten o'clock when we parted here at the restaurant door."

12 "Did pretty well out West, didn't you?" asked the policeman.

13 "You bet! I hope Jimmy has done half as well. He was a kind of plodder,³ though, good fellow as he was. I've had to compete with some of the sharpest wits going to get my pile. A man gets in a groove in New York. It takes the West to put a razor edge on him."

14 The policeman twirled his club and took a step or two.

15 "I'll be on my way. Hope your friend comes around all right. Going to call time on him sharp?"⁴

16 "I should say not!" said the other. "I'll give him half an hour at least. If Jimmy is alive on earth, he'll be here by that time. So long, officer."

---

2. **corresponded.** Communicated by letter
3. **plodder.** One who works slowly and monotonously; a drudge
4. call **time on him sharp.** Leave if he doesn't arrive exactly on time

FIRST READ

Use Reading Skills
Analyze Cause and Effect Why is the man waiting in the doorway?

FIRST READ

Use Reading Skills
Analyze Cause and Effect Why did the two friends lose contact?

staunch•est (stônch′ est) *adj.,* most loyal or committed

FIRST READ

Use Reading Skills
Make Predictions Will the man's old partner show up? If so, will the man really think it was worth the effort?

17   "Good night sir," said the policeman, passing on along his beat, trying doors as he went.

18   There was now a fine, cold drizzle falling, and the wind had risen from its uncertain puffs into a steady blow. The few foot passengers astir in that quarter hurried dismally and silently along with coat collars turned high and pocketed hands. And in the door of the hardware store the man who had come a thousand miles to fill an appointment, uncertain almost to absurdity, with the friend of his youth, smoked his cigar and waited.

19   About twenty minutes he waited, and then a tall man in a long overcoat, with collar turned up to his ears, hurried across from the opposite side of the street. He went directly to the waiting man.

20   "Is that you, Bob?" he asked, doubtfully.

21   "Is that you, Jimmy Wells?" cried the man in the door.

22   "Bless my heart!" exclaimed the new arrival, grasping both the other's hands with his own. "It's Bob, sure as fate. I was certain I'd find you here if you were still in existence. Well, well, well!—twenty years is a long time. The old restaurant's gone, Bob; I wish it had lasted, so we could have had another dinner there. How has the West treated you, old man?"

23   "Bully; it has given me everything I asked it for. You've changed lots, Jimmy. I never thought you were so tall by two or three inches."

24   "Oh, I grew a bit after I was twenty."

25   "Doing well in New York, Jimmy?"

26   "Moderately. I have a position in one of the city departments. Come on, Bob; we'll go around to a place I know of and have a good long talk about old times."

27   The two men started up the street, arm in arm. The man from the West, his **egotism** enlarged by success, was beginning to outline the history of his

FIRST READ ➤

Use Reading Skills
Make Predictions Now that the two men have met, what do you think will happen next?

e•go•tism (ē´ gə' ti zəm) *n.,* large sense of self-importance; conceit

career. The other, submerged in his overcoat, listened with interest.

28   At the corner stood a drugstore, brilliant with electric lights. When they came into this glare, each of them turned simultaneously[5] to gaze upon the other's face.

29   The man from the West stopped suddenly and released his arm.

30   "You're not Jimmy Wells," he snapped. "Twenty years is a long time, but not long enough to change a man's nose from a Roman to a pug."[6]

31   "It sometimes changes a good man into a bad one," said the tall man. "You've been under arrest for ten minutes, 'Silky' Bob. Chicago thinks you may have dropped over our way and wires[7] us she wants to have a chat with you. Going quietly, are you? That's sensible. Now, before we go to the station, here's a note I was asked to hand to you. You may read it here at the window. It's from Patrolman Wells."

32   The man from the West unfolded the little piece of paper handed him. His hand was steady when he began to read, but it **trembled** a little by the time he had finished. The note was rather short.

33   *Bob: I was at the appointed place on time. When you struck the match to light your cigar, I saw it was the face of the man wanted in Chicago. Somehow I couldn't do it myself, so I went around and got a plainclothes man to do the job.*

34   *Jimmy*

---

5. **simultaneously.** At the same time
6. **Roman to a pug.** Two distinctly shaped noses
7. wires. Communicates by telegram

← SECOND READ

Analyze Literature
Plot In what way did the setting affect the resolution?

Mirrors & Windows   What circumstances might cause you to do what Jimmy Wells did? What are the limits of loyalty?

_____

_____

_____

_____

Close Reading Model

Find Meaning	Make Judgments
1. (a) How does the narrator describe the policeman? (b) What does this description suggest about this character?	**4.** What does the waiting man's description of Jimmy Wells as a "plodder" suggest about his attitude toward his friend?
2. Why does the man in the doorway feel it is necessary to explain his presence to the policeman?	**5.** Is it surprising that the waiting man traveled a thousand miles for the meeting? Explain.
3. (a) What are the most important details of the setting? (b) Why are these details important?	**6.** What overall message, or theme, do you think O. Henry wanted to convey in "After Twenty Years"?

Analyze Literature

Plot Did you predict the climax and the resolution of the story? Use a plot diagram to identify the exposition, climax, and resolution of "After Twenty Years."

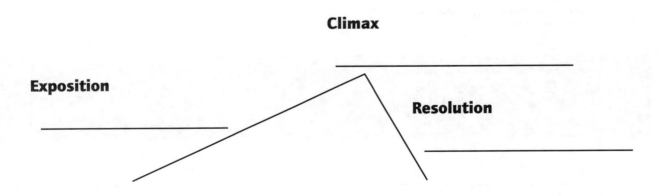

Climax

Exposition

Resolution

Writing Connection

Informative Writing The plainclothes policeman tells Bob that twenty years is long enough to change "a good man into a bad one." Using your cause-and-effect chart, write a short **essay** in which you analyze the causes and effects that brought Bob to justice in "After Twenty Years." Cite evidence from the text to support your arguments.

The 11:59 _{page 15}

SHORT STORY by Patricia McKissack

Historical Context The Pullman sleeping car was introduced in 1865 to provide train passengers with comfortable sleeping quarters for overnight trips. Pullman porters tended to the sleeping quarters, carried luggage, and assisted passengers. For nearly a century, these porters were almost exclusively African American.

Reader's Context What if you had only a few more hours to live? What would you do or think about in those last few hours?

_____

_____

Set Purpose

Preview the title of the story. Then read to determine what significance the title has for the story's main character.

Analyze Literature

Character Writers make careful choices about how they describe a story's **main character,** or **protagonist.** The changes that a character undergoes during a story can help to reveal the writer's message, or theme, to the reader. As you read "The 11:59," pay attention to how the writer presents the main character and think about what you learn from his behavior and feelings.

Use Reading Skills

Take Notes When you read a short story, it can be helpful to take notes. Writing down the names of the main characters and their traits, details of the story's setting and conflict, and the outcome of the events described can all help you better understand what you have read. As you read "The 11:59," take notes in a chart like the one below.

Characters	Setting	Conflict
Lester Simmons		

FIRST READ ➝

Use Reading Skills
Take Notes What trait do you notice about Lester right away?

SECOND READ ➝

Analyze Literature
Character What can you tell about Lester based on how he spends his time?

A Short Story by Patricia McKissack

The 11:59
Ticktock, ticktock.

1 Lester Simmons was a thirty-year retired Pullman car porter—had his gold watch to prove it. "Keeps perfect train time," he often bragged. "Good to the second."

2 Daily he went down to the St. Louis Union Station and shined shoes to help supplement[1] his **meager** twenty-four-dollar-a-month Pullman retirement check. He ate his evening meal at the porter house on Compton Avenue and hung around until late at night talking union, playing bid whist,[2] and spinning yarns with those who were still "travelin' men." In this way Lester stayed in touch with the only family he'd known since 1920.

3 There was nothing the young porters liked more than listening to Lester tell true stories about the old days, during the founding of the Brotherhood of Sleeping Car Porters, the first black union in the United States. He knew the president, A. Philip Randolph, personally, and proudly boasted that it was Randolph who'd signed him up as a union man back in 1926. He passed his original card around for inspection. "I knew all the founding brothers. Take Brother E. J. Bradley. We hunted many a day together, not for the sport of it but for something to eat. Those were hard times, starting up the union. But we hung in there so you youngsters might have the benefits you enjoy now."

4 The rookie porters always liked hearing about the thirteen-year struggle between the Brotherhood and the powerful Pullman Company, and how, against all odds, the fledgling[3] union had won recognition and better working conditions.

5 Everybody enjoyed it too when Lester told tall tales about Daddy Joe, the porters' larger-than-life hero. "Now y'all know the first thing a good Pullman man is expected to do is make up the top and lower berths[4] for the passengers each night."

6 "Come on, Lester," one of his listeners **chided**. "You don't need to describe our jobs for us."

7 "Some of you, maybe not. But some of you, well—" he said, looking over the top of his glasses and raising an eyebrow at a

chide (chīd) *v.*, express mild disapproval

SECOND READ ➝

Analyze Literature
Character What does the dialogue between Lester and the younger porters suggest about Lester's character?

---

1. **supplement.** Add to
2. **bid whist.** Card game played with partners
3. fledgling. Inexperienced
4. berths. Places for sleeping

few of the younger porters. "I was just setting the stage." He smiled good-naturedly and went on with his story. "They tell me Daddy Joe could walk flatfooted down the center of the coach and let down berths on both sides of the aisle."

8   Hearty laughter filled the room, because everyone knew that to accomplish such a feat, Daddy Joe would have to have been superhuman. But that was it: To the men who worked the sleeping cars, Daddy Joe was no less a hero than Paul Bunyan was to the lumberjacks of the Northwestern forests.

9   "And when the 11:59 pulled up to his door, as big and strong as Daddy Joe was..." Lester continued solemnly. "Well, in the end even he couldn't escape the 11:59." The old story-teller eyed one of the rookie porters he knew had never heard the frightening tale about the porters' Death Train. Lester took joy in **mesmerizing** his young listeners with all the details.

10   "Any porter who hears the whistle of the 11:59 has got exactly twenty-four hours to clear up earthly matters. He better be ready when the train comes the next night..." In his creakiest voice, Lester drove home the point. "All us porters got to board that train one day. Ain't no way to escape the final ride on the 11:59."

11   *Silence.*

12   "Lester," a young porter asked, "you know anybody who ever heard the whistle of the 11:59 and lived to tell—"

13   "Not a living soul!"

14   *Laughter.*

15   "Well," began one of the men, "wonder will we have to make up berths on *that* train?"

16   "If it's an overnight trip to heaven, you can best be believing there's bound to be a few of us making up the berths," another answered.

17   "Shucks," a card player stopped to put in. "They say even up in heaven *we* the ones gon' be keeping all that gold and silver polished."

SECOND READ

Analyze Literature
Character Is Daddy Joe a flat, one-dimensional character or a round, fully developed character?

mes•mer•ize (mez´ mə rīz´) v., fascinate, spellbind

SECOND READ ➤

Analyze Character
Character What do you think Lester's co-workers thought of him during his career?

SECOND READ ➤

Use Reading Skills
Context Clues What is *finery*? Use context clues in the surrounding text to determine the meaning of the word. What clues help you determine the words meaning?

wor • ri • some (wʉr´ ē səm) *adj.*, causing worry

SECOND READ ➤

Analyze Literature
Character What character traits does Lester reveal about himself in telling how he gave Tip his nickname? Explain.

FIRST READ ➤

Use Reading Skills
Make Predictions What might this reference to Tip foreshadow?

18   "Speaking of gold and silver," Lester said, remembering. "That reminds me of how I gave Tip Sampson his nickname. Y'all know Tip?"

19   There were plenty of nods and smiles.

20   The memory made Lester chuckle. He shifted in his seat to find a more comfortable spot. Then he began. "A woman got on board the *Silver Arrow* in Chicago going to Los Angeles. She was dripping in finery—had on all kinds of gold and diamond jewelry, carried twelve bags. Sampson knocked me down getting to wait on her, figuring she was sure for a big tip. That lady was **worrisome**! Ooowee! 'Come do this. Go do that. Bring me this.'

21   Sampson was running over himself trying to keep that lady happy. When we reached L.A., my passengers all tipped me two or three dollars, as was customary back then.

22   "When Sampson's Big Money lady got off, she reached into her purse and placed a dime in his outstretched hand. A *dime!* Can you imagine? *Ow!* You should have seen his face. And I didn't make it no better. Never did let him forget it. I teased him so—went to calling him Tip, and the nickname stuck."

23   *Laughter.*

24   "I haven't heard from ol' Tip in a while. Anybody know anything?"

25   "You haven't got word, Lester? Tip boarded the 11:59 over in Kansas City about a month ago."

26   "Sorry to hear that. That just leaves me and Willie Beavers, the last of the old, old-timers here in St. Louis."

27   Lester looked at his watch—it was a little before midnight. The talkfest had lasted later than usual. He said his good-byes and left, taking his usual route across the Eighteenth Street bridge behind the station.

28   In the darkness, Lester looked over the yard, picking out familiar shapes—the *Hummingbird,* the *Zephyr.* He'd worked on them both. Train travel wasn't anything like it used to be in the old days—not since people had begun to ride airplanes. "Progress," he scoffed. "Those contraptions will never take the place of a train. No sir!"

29   Suddenly he felt a sharp pain in his chest. At exactly the same moment he heard the mournful sound of a train whistle, which the wind seemed to carry from some faraway place. Ignoring his pain, Lester looked at the old station. He knew nothing was scheduled to come in or out till early morning.

Nervously he lit a match to check the time. 11:59!

30   "No," he said into the darkness. "I'm not ready. I've got plenty of living yet."

31   Fear quickened his step. Reaching his small apartment, he hurried up the steps. His heart pounded in his ear, and his left arm tingled. He had an idea, and there wasn't a moment to waste. But his own words haunted him. *Ain't no way to escape the final ride on the 11:59.*

32   "But I'm gon' try!" Lester spent the rest of the night plotting his escape from fate.

33   "I won't eat or drink anything all day," he talked himself through his plan. "That way I can't choke, die of food poisoning, or cause a cooking fire."

34   Lester shut off the space heater to avoid an explosion, nailed shut all doors and windows to keep out intruders, and unplugged every electrical appliance. Good weather was predicted, but just in case a freak storm came and blew out a window, shooting deadly glass shards in his direction, he moved a straight-backed chair into a far corner, making sure nothing was overhead to fall on him.

35   "I'll survive," he said, smiling at the prospect of beating Death. "Won't that be a wonderful story to tell at the porter house?" He rubbed his left arm. It felt numb again.

36   Lester sat silently in his chair all day, too afraid to move. At noon someone knocked on his door. He couldn't answer it. Footsteps...another knock. He didn't answer.

37   A parade of minutes passed by, equally measured, one behind the other, ticking...ticking...away...The dull pain in his chest returned. He nervously checked his watch every few minutes.

38   *Ticktock, ticktock.*

39   Time had always been on his side. Now it was his enemy. Where had the years gone? Lester reviewed the thirty years he'd spent riding the rails. How different would his life have been if he'd married Louise Henderson and had a gallon of children? What if he'd taken that job at the mill down in Opelika? What if he'd followed his brother to Philly? How different?

40   *Ticktock, ticktock.*

41   So much living had passed so quickly. Lester decided if he had to do it all over again, he'd stand by his choices. His had been a good life. No regrets. No major changes for him.

FIRST READ

Use Reading Skills
Take Notes What is this story's conflict? What do you think the outcome will be?

SECOND READ

Analyze Literature
Character What is Lester's motivation for refusing to answer the door?

FIRST READ

Make Connections
How does Lester's judgment about his life affect your feelings about what is happening to him?

42   *Ticktock, ticktock.*

43   The times he'd had—both good and bad—what memories. His first and only love had been traveling, and she was a jealous companion. Wonder whatever happened to that girl up in Minneapolis? Thinking about her made him smile. Then he laughed. That *girl* must be close to seventy years old by now.

44   *Ticktock, ticktock.*

45   Daylight was fading quickly. Lester drifted off to sleep, then woke from a nightmare in which, like Jonah, he'd been swallowed by an enormous beast.[5] Even awake he could still hear its heart beating...*ticktock, ticktock*...But then he realized he was hearing his own heartbeat.

46   Lester couldn't see his watch, but he guessed no more than half an hour had passed. Sleep had overtaken him with such little resistance. Would Death, that shapeless shadow, slip in that easily? Where was he lurking? *Yea, though I walk through the valley of the shadow of death, I will fear no evil...*The Twenty-third Psalm was the only prayer Lester knew, and he repeated it over and over, hoping it would comfort him.

47   Lester rubbed his tingling arm. He could hear the blood rushing past his ear and up the side of his head. He longed to know what time it was, but that meant he had to light a match—too risky. What if there was a gas leak? The match would set off an explosion. "I'm too smart for that, Death," he said.

48   *Ticktock, ticktock.*

49   It was late. He could feel it. Stiffness seized his legs and made them tremble. How much longer? he wondered. Was he close to winning?

50   Then in the fearful silence he heard a train whistle. His ears strained to identify the sound, making sure it *was* a whistle. No mistake. It came again, the same as the night before. Lester answered it with a groan.

51   *Ticktock, ticktock.*

52   He could hear Time ticking away in his head. Gas leak or not, he had to see his watch. Striking a match, Lester quickly checked the time. 11:57.

53   Although there was no gas explosion, a tiny explosion erupted in his heart.

54   *Ticktock, ticktock.*

55   Just a little more time. The whistle sounded again. Closer

---

5. Jonah...beast. Refers to the biblical story of Jonah and the whale

than before. Lester struggled to move, but he felt fastened to the chair. Now he could hear the engine puffing, pulling a heavy load. It was hard for him to breathe, too, and the pain in his chest weighed heavier and heavier.

56   *Ticktock, ticktock.*

57   Time had run out! Lester's mind reached for an explanation that made sense. But reason failed when a glowing phantom dressed in the porters' blue uniform stepped out of the grayness of Lester's confusion.

58   "It's *your* time, good brother." The **specter** spoke in a thousand familiar voices.

spec • ter (spek´ tər) *n.*, spirit or ghost

59   Freed of any restraint now, Lester stood, bathed in a peaceful calm that had its own glow. "Is that you, Tip?" he asked, squinting
to focus on his old friend standing in the strange light.

60   "It's me, ol' partner. Come to remind you that none of us can escape the last ride on the 11:59."

61   "I know. I know," Lester said, chuckling. "But man, I had to try."

62   Tip smiled. "I can dig it. So did I."

63   "That'll just leave Willie, won't it?"

64   "Not for long."

65   "I'm ready."

SECOND READ

Analyze Literature
Character Based on what you know about Lester, is his acceptance of his fate surprising? Explain.

66   Lester saw the great beam of the single headlight and heard the deafening whistle blast one last time before the engine tore through the front of the apartment, shattering glass and splintering wood, collapsing everything in its path, including Lester's heart.

67   When Lester didn't show up at the shoeshine stand two days running, friends went over to his place and found him on the floor. His eyes were fixed on something quite amazing— his gold watch, stopped at exactly 11:59. ❖

Mirrors & Windows

Lester tells Tip he "had to try" to fight off Death. Have you ever clung to something you knew you would lose? How can clinging to hope help us come to terms with the inevitable?

_____

_____

_____

_____

Find Meaning	Make Judgments
1. (a) How does Lester spend his evenings after he retires from his job as a Pullman porter? (b) Why does he spend his evenings in this way?	**4.** (a) What does the reader learn about the lives of porters and their relationships with one another from this story? (b) What things did the porters share that reinforced their bonds with one another?
2. (a) What physical symptoms does Lester feel during his last day alive? (b) What do you think is happening to Lester?	**5.** (a) How does Lester's mood change when he first hears the 11:59? (b) What does this mood change tell you about Lester's personality?
3. (a) What time is on Lester's watch when his friends find him two days later? (b) Why does his watch read that time?	**6.** (a) How does Lester feel when he sees who the porter on the 11:59 is? (b) What does the manner in which they talk tell you about Lester's mood or attitude?

Analyze Literature

Character Writers use a variety of techniques to create characters to whom readers can relate and who can convey lessons about life. Use a chart to analyze how the author creates the character of Lester in "The 11:59." Then analyze, in one or two sentences, how the reader is made to feel about Lester at the end of the story.

Lester's Character

Habits/Behaviors	Relationships with Others
hard worker	friendly

Writing Connection

Narrative Writing When friends gather at a funeral, they often take turns telling stories and sharing memories of the departed. Write a **paragraph** about Lester's life and personality that you might share at Lester's funeral with his friends from the porter house. Include an example or an anecdote to illustrate a memorable character trait. Share your work with the class.

The Inn of Lost Time page 26

SHORT STORY by Lensey Namioka

Build Background

Historical Context In feudal Japan (1100s to 1800s), the country was broken up into many domains, each held by a lord, or land baron. The feudal lord's land was protected by samurai, members of the warrior class, who were the only people allowed to carry weapons. This story takes place during the 1700s, a period of famine and civil wars. Many landowners could no longer afford to keep their samurai, and these master-less samurai, or ronin, wandered the countryside looking for work.

Reader's Context Do you ever say things like "I can't wait until I'm older"? What if you could skip years of your life?

_____

_____

Analyze Literature

Setting In addition to physical descriptions of time and place, **setting** also includes the broader cultural, social, and historical background in which a story's characters live and interact. As you read "The Inn of Lost Time," record the setting details that the writer presents and consider the effect that the setting has on the characters and the plot.

Set Purpose

Skim the text and predict what effect the setting of the story will have on the plot. Read to find out if your prediction is accurate.

Use Reading Skills

Sequence of Events As you read "The Inn of Lost Time," use a time line to track the sequence of events. Begin by recording the first events mentioned in the story. Complete the time line by adding the events that occur before and after these events. Look for signal words such as _before_, _after_, _then_, _while_, and _later_.

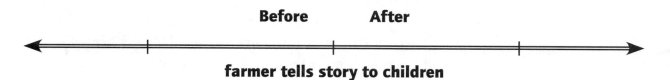

Before   **After**

farmer tells story to children

A Short Story by Lensey Namioka

The Inn of Lost Time

1 Will you promise to sleep if I tell you a story?" said the father. He pretended to put on a stern expression.

2 "Yes! Yes!" the three little boys chanted in unison. It sounded like a nightly routine.

3 The two guests smiled as they listened to the exchange. They were wandering ronin, or unemployed samurai, and they enjoyed watching this cozy family scene.

4 The father gave the guests a helpless look. "What can I do? I have to tell them a story, or these little rascals will give us no peace." Clearing his throat, he turned to the boys. "All right. The story tonight is about Urashima Taro."

5 Instantly the three boys became still. Sitting with their legs tucked under them, the three little boys, aged five, four, and three, looked like a descending row of stone statuettes. Matsuzo, the younger of the two ronin, was reminded of the wayside half-body statues of Jizo, the God of Travelers and Protector of Children.

6 Behind the boys the farmer's wife took up a pair of iron chopsticks and stirred the ashes of the fire in the charcoal brazier.[1] A momentary glow brightened the room. The lean faces of the two ronin, lit by the fire, suddenly looked fierce and hungry.

7 The farmer knew that the two ronin were supposed to use their arms in defense of the weak. But in these troubled times, with the country torn apart by civil wars, the samurai didn't always live up to their honorable code.

8 Then the fire died down again and the subdued red light softened the features of the two ronin. The farmer relaxed and began his story.

9 The tale of Urashima Taro is familiar to every Japanese. No doubt the three little boys had heard their father tell it before—and more than once. But they listened with **rapt** attention.

10 Urashima Taro, a fisherman, rescued a turtle from some boys who were battering it with stones. The grateful turtle rewarded Taro by carrying him on his back to the bottom of the sea, where he lived happily with the Princess of the Underseas. But Taro soon became homesick for his native

SECOND READ

Analyze Literature
Setting What do the details tell you about where the ronin are and when this scene takes place?

rapt (rapt) *adj.*, mentally engrossed or absorbed

---

1. brazier. Pan for holding burning coals

village and asked to go back on land. The princess gave
him a box to take with him but warned him not to peek
11 inside.

When Taro went back to his village, he found the place
quite changed. In his home he found his parents gone and
living there was another old couple. He was stunned to learn
that the aged husband was his own son whom he had last seen
as a baby. Taro thought he had spent only a pleasant week or
two undersea with the princess. On land, seventy-two years
had passed! His parents and most of his old friends had long
12 since died.

Desolate, Taro decided to open the box given him by the
princess. As soon as he looked inside he changed in an instant
13 from a young man to a decrepit² old man of more than ninety.

At the end of the story the boys were close to tears. Even
Matsuzo found himself deeply touched. He wondered why
the farmer had told his sons such a **poignant** bedtime story.
14 Wouldn't they worry all evening instead of going to sleep?

But the boys recovered quickly. They were soon laughing
and jostling each other, and they made no objections when
their mother shooed them toward bed. Standing in order of
age, they bowed politely to the guests, and then lay down
on the mattresses spread out for them on the floor. Within
minutes the sound of their regular breathing told the guests
15 that they were asleep.

Zenta, the older of the two ronin, sighed as he glanced at
the peaceful young faces. "I wish I could fall asleep so quickly.
The story of Urashima Taro is one of the saddest that I know
16 among our folk tales."

The farmer looked proudly at his sleeping sons. "They're
17 stout lads. Nothing bothers them much."

The farmer's wife poured tea for the guests and apologized. "I'm sorry this is only poor tea made from coarse
18 leaves."

Zenta hastened to reassure her. "It's warm and heartening
19 on a chilly autumn evening."

"You know what I think is the saddest part of the
Urashima Taro story?" said Matsuzo, picking up his cup and
sipping the tea. "It's that Taro lost not only his family and
friends, but a big piece of his life as well. He had lost the most
precious thing of all: time."

---

2. **decrepit.** Broken down; weak

des•o•late (de´ sə lət) *adj.*, lonely, sad

poi•gnant (poi´ nyənt) *adj.*, deeply
affecting or touching; somber

SECOND READ

Analyze Literature
Setting Based on the details in this
passage, what can you infer about the
farmer's house?

20   The farmer nodded agreement. "I wouldn't sell even one year of my life for money. As for losing seventy-two years, no amount of gold will make up for that!"

21   Zenta put his cup down on the floor and looked curiously at the farmer. "It's interesting that you should say that. I had an opportunity once to observe exactly how much gold a person was willing to pay for some lost years of his life." He smiled grimly. "In this case the man went as far as one gold piece for each year he lost."

22   "That's bizarre!" said Matsuzo. "You never told me about it."

23   "It happened long before I met you," said Zenta. He drank some tea and smiled ruefully.[3] "Besides, I'm not particularly proud of the part I played in that strange affair."

24   "Let's hear the story!" urged Matsuzo. "You've made us all curious."

25   The farmer waited expectantly. His wife sat down quietly behind her husband and folded her hands. Her eyes looked intently at Zenta.

26   "Very well, then," said Zenta. "Actually, my story bears some resemblance to that of Urashima Taro..."

27   It happened about seven years ago, when I was a green, inexperienced youngster not quite eighteen years old. But I had had a good training in arms, and I was able to get a job as a bodyguard for a wealthy merchant from Sakai.

28   As you know, wealthy merchants are relatively new in our country. Traditionally the rich have been noblemen, landowners, and warlords with thousands of followers. Merchants, considered as parasites[4] in our society, are a despised class. But our civil wars have made people unusually mobile and stimulated trade between various parts of the country. The merchants have taken advantage of this to conduct businesses on a scale our fathers could not imagine. Some of them have become more wealthy than a warlord with thousands of samurai under his command.

29   The man I was escorting,[5] Tokubei, was one of this new breed of wealthy merchants. He was trading not only with outlying provinces but even with the Portuguese from across the sea. On this particular journey he was not carrying much gold with him. If he had, I'm sure he would have hired an older and more experienced bodyguard. But if the need

FIRST READ

Use Reading Skills
Sequence of Events When did the events of Zenta's story take place?

SECOND READ

Analyze Literature
Setting What do these details reveal about the Japanese society that serves as a background for the story?

---

3. **ruefully.** In a regretful way
4. **parasites.** People who make a habit of taking advantage of others
5. **escorting.** Accompanying; guiding

should arise, he could always write a message to his clerks at home and have money forwarded to him. It's important to remember this.

30   The second day of our journey was a particularly grueling one, with several steep hills to climb. As the day was drawing to its close, we began to consider where we should spend the night. I knew that within an hour's walking was a hot-spring resort known to have several attractive inns.

31   But Tokubei, my employer, said he was already very tired and wanted to stop. He had heard of the resort, and knew the inns there were expensive. Wealthy as he was, he did not want to spend more money than he had to.

32   While we stood talking, a smell reached our noses, a wonderful smell of freshly cooked rice. Suddenly I felt **ravenous**. From the way Tokubei swallowed, I knew he was feeling just as hungry.

rav•en•ous (raˊ və nəs) *adj.,* very eager for food

33   We looked around eagerly, but the area was forested and we could not see very far in any direction. The tantalizing smell seemed to grow and I could feel the saliva filling my mouth.

34   "There's an inn around here, somewhere," muttered Tokubei. "I'm sure of it."

35   We followed our noses. We had to leave the well-traveled highway and take a narrow, winding footpath. But the mouth-watering smell of the rice and the vision of fluffy, freshly aired cotton quilts drew us on.

SECOND READ

Analyze Literature
Setting How does the imagery in this passage explain why Tokubei and Zenta leave the highway to search for an unknown inn?

36   The sun was just beginning to set. We passed a bamboo grove, and in the low evening light the thin leaves turned into little golden knives. I saw a gilded clump of bamboo shoots. The sight made me think of the delicious dish they would make when boiled in soy sauce.

37   We hurried forward. To our delight we soon came to a clearing with a thatched house standing in the middle. The fragrant smell of rice was now so strong that we were certain a meal was being prepared inside.

38   Standing in front of the house was a pretty girl beaming at us with a welcoming smile. "Please honor us with your presence," she said, beckoning.

39   There was something a little unusual about one of her hands, but, being hungry and eager to enter the house, I did not stop to observe closely.

SECOND READ

Analyze Literature
Setting What is odd about the location of the inn? Why isn't Zenta suspicious?

40   You will say, of course, that it was my duty as a body-guard to be suspicious and to look out for danger. Youth and inexperience should not have prevented me from wondering why an inn should be found hidden away from the highway. As it was, my stomach growled, and I didn't even hesitate but followed Tokubei to the house.

41   Before stepping up to enter, we were given basins of water to wash our feet. As the girl handed us towels for drying, I saw what was unusual about her left hand: she had six fingers.

42   Tokubei had noticed it as well. When the girl turned away to empty the basins, he nudged me. "Did you see her left hand? She had—" He broke off in confusion as the girl turned around, but she didn't seem to have heard.

43   The inn was peaceful and quiet, and we soon discovered the reason why. We were the only guests. Again, I should have been suspicious. I told you that I'm not proud of the part I played.

44   Tokubei turned to me and grinned. "It seems that there are no other guests. We should be able to get extra service for the same amount of money."

45   The girl led us to a spacious room which was like the principal chamber of a private residence. Cushions were set out for us on the floor and we began to shed our traveling gear to make ourselves comfortable.

46   The door opened and a grizzled-haired man entered. Despite his vigorous-looking[6] face his back was a little bent and I guessed his age to be about fifty. After bowing and greeting us he apologized in advance for the service. "We have not always been innkeepers here," he said, "and you may find the accommodations lacking. Our good intentions must make up for our inexperience. However, to **compensate** for our inadequacies,[7] we will charge a lower fee than that of an inn with an established reputation."

47   Tokubei nodded graciously, highly pleased by the words of our host, and the evening began well. It continued well when the girl came back with some flasks of wine, cups, and dishes of salty snacks.

48   While the girl served the wine, the host looked with interest at my swords. From the few remarks he made, I gath

com•pen•sate (käm´ pən sāt') v.,
balance, offset, repay

---

6. **vigorous.** Lively; energetic
7. **inadequacies.** Shortcomings

Close Reading

ered that he was a former samurai, forced by circumstances to turn his house into an inn.

49   Having become a bodyguard to a tight-fisted merchant,
I was in no position to feel superior to a ronin turned
innkeeper. Socially, therefore, we were more or less equal.

50   We exchanged polite remarks with our host while we
drank and tasted the salty snacks. I looked around at the
pleasant room. It showed excellent taste, and I especially
admired a vase standing in the alcove.

51   My host caught my eyes on it. "We still have a few good
things that we didn't have to sell," he said. His voice held a
trace of bitterness. "Please look at the panels of these doors.
They were painted by a fine artist."

52   Tokubei and I looked at the pair of sliding doors.
Each panel contained a landscape painting, the right panel
depicting a winter scene and the left one the same scene in late
summer. Our host's words were no idle[8] boast. The pictures
were indeed beautiful.

53   Tokubei rose and approached the screens
for a closer look. When he sat down again, his
eyes were calculating. No doubt he was
trying to estimate what price the
paintings would fetch.

54   After my third drink I began to feel very tired.
Perhaps it was the result of drinking on an empty
stomach. I was glad when the girl brought in two dinner
trays and a lacquered container of rice. Uncovering the
rice container, she began filling our bowls.

55   Again I noticed her strange left hand with its
six fingers. Any other girl would have tried to keep
that hand hidden, but this girl made no effort to do so. If
anything, she seemed to use that hand more than her other
one when she served us. The extra little finger always stuck
out from the hand, as if inviting comment.

56   The hand fascinated me so much that I kept my eyes
on it, and soon forgot to eat. After a while the hand looked
blurry. And then everything else began to look blurry. The
last thing I remembered was the sight of Tokubei shaking his
head, as if trying to clear it.

---

8. idle. Without worth or basis in fact

FIRST READ ➤

Use Reading Skills
Sequence of Events Zenta has three drinks and the girl serves the rice. What happens after that?

57 When I opened my eyes again, I knew that time had passed, but not how much time. My next thought was that it was cold. It was not only extremely cold but damp.

58 I rolled over and sat up. I reached immediately for my swords and found them safe on the ground beside me. On the ground? What was I doing on the ground? My last memory was of staying at an inn with a merchant called Tokubei.

59 The thought of Tokubei put me into a panic. I was his bodyguard, and instead of watching over him, I had fallen asleep and had awakened in a strange place.

60 I looked around frantically and saw that he was lying on the ground not far from where I was. Had he been killed?

61 I got up shakily, and when I stood up my head was swimming. But my sense of urgency gave some strength to my legs. I stumbled over to my employer and to my great relief found him breathing—breathing heavily, in fact.

62 When I shook his shoulder, he grunted and finally opened his eyes. "Where am I?" he asked thickly.

63 It was a reasonable question. I looked around and saw that we had been lying in a bamboo grove. By the light I guessed that it was early morning, and the reason I felt cold and damp was because my clothes were wet with dew.

64 "It's cold!" said Tokubei, shivering and climbing unsteadily to his feet. He looked around slowly, and his eyes became wide with disbelief. "What happened? I thought we were staying at an inn!"

65 His words came as a relief. One of the possibilities I had considered was that I had gone mad and that the whole episode with the inn was something I had imagined. Now I knew that Tokubei had the same memory of the inn. I had not imagined it.

66 But why were we out here on the cold ground, instead of on comfortable mattresses in the inn?

67 "They must have drugged us and robbed us," said Tokubei. He turned and looked at me furiously. "A fine bodyguard you are!"

68 There was nothing I could say to that. But at least we were both alive and unharmed. "Did they take all your money?" I asked.

69 Tokubei had already taken his wallet out of his sash and was peering inside. "That's funny! My money is still here!"

CLOSE READ ➤

Make Connections
What assumption would you make if you found yourself in this situation?

70   This was certainly unexpected. What did the innkeeper and his strange daughter intend to do by drugging us and moving us outside?

71   At least things were not as bad as we had feared. We had not lost anything except a comfortable night's sleep, although from the heaviness in my head I had certainly slept deeply enough—and long enough too. Exactly how much time had elapsed[9] since we drank wine with our host?

72   All we had to do now was find the highway again and continue our journey. Tokubei suddenly chuckled. "I didn't even have to pay for our night's lodging!"

73   As we walked from the bamboo grove, I saw the familiar clump of bamboo shoots, and we found ourselves standing in the same clearing again. Before our eyes was the thatched house. Only it was somehow different. Perhaps things looked different in the daylight than at dusk.

74   But the difference was more than a change of light. As we approached the house slowly, like sleepwalkers, we saw that the thatching was much darker. On the previous evening the thatching had looked fresh and new. Now it was dark with age. Daylight should make things appear brighter, not darker. The plastering of the walls also looked more dingy.[10]

75   Tokubei and I stopped to look at each other before we went closer. He was pale, and I knew that I looked no less frightened. Something was terribly wrong. I loosened my sword in its scabbard.

76   We finally gathered the courage to go up to the house. Since Tokubei seemed unable to find his voice, I spoke out. "Is anyone there?"

77   After a moment we heard shuffling footsteps and the front door slid open. The face of an old woman appeared. "Yes?" she inquired. Her voice was creaky with age.

78   What set my heart pounding with panic, however, was not her voice. It was the sight of her left hand holding on to the frame of the door. The hand was wrinkled and crooked with the arthritis of old age—and it had six fingers.

79   I heard a gasp beside me and knew that Tokubei had noticed the hand as well.

80   The door opened wider and a man appeared beside the old woman. At first I thought it was our host of the previous

NOTES

SECOND READ

Analyze Literature
Setting What is different about the outside of the house?

---

9. elapsed. Passed
10. dingy. Dirty or discolored; showing signs of wear or neglect

night. But this man was much younger, although the resemblance was strong. He carried himself straighter and his hair was black, while the innkeeper had been grizzled and slightly bent with age.

81   "Please excuse my mother," said the man. "Her hearing is not good. Can we help you in some way?"

82   Tokubei finally found his voice. "Isn't this the inn where we stayed last night?"

83   The man stared. "Inn? We are not innkeepers here!"

84   "Yes, you are!" insisted Tokubei. "Your daughter invited us in and served us with wine. You must have put something in the wine!"

85   The man frowned. "You are serious? Are you sure you didn't drink too much at your inn and wander off?"

86   "No, I didn't drink too much!" said Tokubei, almost shouting. "I hardly drank at all! Your daughter, the one with six fingers in her hand, started to pour me a second cup of wine..." His voice trailed off, and he stared again at the left hand of the old woman.

87   "I don't have a daughter," said the man slowly. "My mother here is the one who has six fingers in her left hand, although I hardly think it polite of you to mention it."

88   "I'm getting dizzy," muttered Tokubei and began to totter.

89   "I think you'd better come in and rest a bit," the man said to him gruffly. He glanced at me. "Perhaps you wish to join your friend. You don't share his delusion[11] about the inn, I hope?"

90   "I wouldn't presume to contradict my elders," I said carefully. Since both Tokubei and the owner of the house were my elders, I wasn't committing myself. In truth I didn't know what to believe, but I did want a look at the inside of the house.

91   The inside was almost the same as it was before but the differences were there when I looked closely. We entered the same room with the alcove and the pair of painted doors. The vase I had admired was no longer there, but the doors showed the same landscapes painted by a master. I peered closely at the pictures and saw that the colors looked faded. What was more, the left panel, the one depicting a winter scene, had a long tear in one corner. It had been painstakingly mended, but the damage was impossible to hide completely.

---

11. **delusion.** Incorrect perception of reality

92   Tokubei saw what I was staring at and he became even paler. At this stage we had both considered the possibility that a hoax of some sort had been played on us. The torn screen convinced Tokubei that our host had not played a joke: the owner of a valuable painting would never vandalize it for a trivial reason.

93   As for me, I was far more disturbed by the sight of the sixth finger on the old woman's hand. Could the young girl have disguised herself as an old crone? She could put rice powder in her hair to whiten it, but she could not transform her pretty straight fingers into old fingers twisted with arthritis. The woman here with us now was genuinely old, at least fifty years older than the girl.

94   It was this same old woman who finally gave us our greatest shock. "It's interesting that you should mention an inn, gentlemen," she croaked. "My father used to operate an inn. After he died, my husband and I turned this back into a private residence. We didn't need the income, you see."

95   "Your...your...f-father?" stammered Tokubei.

96   "Yes," replied the old woman. "He was a ronin, forced to go into innkeeping when he lost his position. But he never liked the work. Besides, our inn had begun to acquire an unfortunate reputation. Some of our guests disappeared, you see."

97   Even before she finished speaking, a horrible suspicion had begun to dawn on me. Her father had been an innkeeper, she said, her father who used to be a ronin. The man who had been our host was a ronin turned innkeeper. Could this mean that this old woman was actually the same person as the young girl we had seen?

98   I sat stunned while I tried to absorb the implications. What had happened to us? Was it possible that Tokubei and I had slept while this young girl grew into a mature woman, got married, and bore a son, a son who was now an adult? If that was the case, then we had slept for fifty years!

99   The old woman's next words confirmed my fears. "I recognize you now! You are two of the lost guests from our inn! The other lost ones I don't remember so well, but I remember you because your disappearance made me so sad. Such a handsome youth, I thought, what a pity that he should have gone the way of the others!"

SECOND READ

Analyze Literature
Setting What detail in the house convinces Tokubei that the host is not just playing a joke? Explain.

FIRST READ

Use Reading Skills
Sequence of Events What sequence of events is suggested to Zenta by the old woman's words?

100   A high wail came from Tokubei, who began to keen[12] and rock himself back and forth. "I've lost fifty years! Fifty years of my life went by while I slept at this accursed inn!"

101   The inn was indeed accursed. Was the fate of the other guests similar to ours? "Did anyone else return as we did, fifty years later?" I asked.

102   The old woman looked uncertain and turned to her son. He frowned thoughtfully. "From time to time wild-looking people have come to us with stories similar to yours. Some of them went mad with the shock."

103   Tokubei wailed again. "I've lost my business! I've lost my wife, my young and beautiful wife! We had been married only a couple of months!"

104   A gruesome chuckle came from the old woman. "You may not have lost your wife. It's just that she's become an old hag like me!"

105   That did not console Tokubei, whose keening became louder. Although my relationship with my employer had not been characterized by much respect on either side, I did begin to feel very sorry for him. He was right: he had lost his world.

106   As for me, the loss was less traumatic.[13] I had left home under extremely painful circumstances, and had spent the next three years wandering. I had no friends and no one I could call a relation. The only thing I had was my duty to my employer. Somehow, some way, I had to help him.

107   "Did no one find an explanation for these disappearances?" I asked. "Perhaps if we knew the reason why, we might find some way to reverse the process."

108   The old woman began to nod eagerly. "The priestess! Tell them about the shrine priestess!"

109   "Well," said the man, "I'm not sure if it would work in your case...."

110   "What? What would work?" demanded Tokubei. His eyes were feverish.

111   "There was a case of one returning guest who consulted the priestess at our local shrine," said the man. "She went into a trance and revealed that there was an evil spirit dwelling in the bamboo grove here. This spirit would put unwary[14] travelers into a long, unnatural sleep. They would wake up twenty, thirty, or even fifty years later."

---

12. keen. Lament or complain loudly
13. traumatic. Shocking
14. unwary. Easily fooled

112   "Yes, but you said something worked in his case," said Tokubei.

113   The man seemed reluctant to go on. "I don't like to see you cheated, so I'm not sure I should be telling you this."

114   "Tell me! Tell me!" demanded Tokubei. The host's reluctance only made him more impatient.

115   "The priestess promised to make a spell that would undo the work of the evil spirit," said the man. "But she demanded a large sum of money, for she said that she had to burn some very rare and costly incense before she could begin the spell."

SECOND READ

Analyze Literature
Setting What do the details about the evil spirit reveal about people's beliefs in this time and place?

116   At the mention of money Tokubei sat back. The hectic flush died down on his face and his eyes narrowed. "How much money?" he asked.

117   The host shook his head. "In my opinion the priestess is a fraud[15] and makes outrageous claims about her powers. We try to have as little to do with her as possible."

118   "Yes, but did her spell work?" asked Tokubei. "If it worked, she's no fraud!"

119   "At least the stranger disappeared again," cackled the old woman. "Maybe he went back to his own time. Maybe he walked into a river."

120   Tokubei's eyes narrowed further. "How much money did the priestess demand?" he asked again.

121   "I think it was one gold piece for every year lost," said the host. He hurriedly added, "Mind you, I still wouldn't trust the priestess."

122   "Then it would cost me fifty gold pieces to get back to my own time," muttered Tokubei. He looked up. "I don't carry that much money with me."

123   "No, you don't," agreed the host.

124   Something alerted me about the way he said that. It was as if the host knew already that Tokubei did not carry much money on him.

125   Meanwhile Tokubei sighed. He had come to a decision. "I do have the means to obtain more money, however. I can send a message to my chief clerk and he will remit[16] the money when he sees my seal."

126   "Your chief clerk may be dead by now," I reminded him.

127   "You're right!" moaned Tokubei. "My business will be under a new management and nobody will even remember my name!"

---

15. fraud. One who cheats or deceives
16. remit. Send (money)

FIRST READ

Use Reading Strategies
Clarify The Latin phrase *carpe diem* applies to this story. Identify the meaning of this foreign phrase and explain how it fits with this section of the story.

128   "And your wife will have remarried," said the old woman, with one of her chuckles. I found it hard to believe that the gentle young girl who had served us wine could turn into this dreadful harridan.[17]

129   "Sending the message may be a waste of time," agreed the host.

130   "What waste of time!" cried Tokubei. "Why shouldn't I waste time? I've wasted fifty years already! Anyway, I've made up my mind. I'm sending that message."

131   "I still think you shouldn't trust the priestess," said the host.

132   That only made Tokubei all the more determined to send for the money. However, he was not quite resigned to the amount. "Fifty gold pieces is a large sum. Surely the priestess can buy incense for less than that amount?"

133   "Why don't you try giving her thirty gold pieces?" cackled the old woman. "Then the priestess will send you back thirty years, and your wife will only be middle-aged."

134   While Tokubei was still arguing with himself about the exact sum to send for, I decided to have a look at the bamboo grove. "I'm going for a walk," I announced, rising and picking up my sword from the floor beside me.

135   The host turned sharply to look at me. For an instant a faint, rueful smile appeared on his lips. Then he looked away.

136   Outside, I went straight to the clump of shoots in the bamboo grove. On the previous night—or what I perceived as the previous night—I had noticed that clump of bamboo shoots particularly, because I had been so hungry that I pictured them being cut up and boiled.

137   The clump of bamboo shoots was still in the same place. That in itself proved nothing, since bamboo could spring up anywhere, including the place where a clump had existed fifty years earlier. But what settled the matter in my mind was that the clump looked almost exactly the way it did when I had seen it before, except that every shoot was about an inch taller. That was a reasonable amount for bamboo shoots to grow overnight.

138   Overnight. Tokubei and I had slept on the ground here overnight. We had not slept here for a period of fifty years.

139   Once I knew that, I was able to see another inconsistency: the door panels with the painted landscapes. The painting

FIRST READ

Use Reading Skills
Sequence of Events What inconsistency does Zenta discover in the old woman's story of lost time?

---

17. harridan. Ill-tempered woman

with the winter scene had been on the right last night and it was on the left this morning. It wasn't simply a case of the panels changing places, because the depressions in the panel for the handholds had been reversed. In other words, what I saw just now was not a pair of paintings faded and torn by age. They were an entirely different pair of paintings.

140   But how did the pretty young girl change into an old woman? The answer was that if the screens could be different ones, so could the women. I had seen one woman, a young girl, last night. This morning I saw a different woman, an old hag.

141   The darkening of the thatched roof? Simply blow ashes over the roof. The grizzled-haired host of last night could be the same man who claimed to be his grandson today. It would be a simple matter for a young man to put gray in his hair and assume a stoop.

142   And the purpose of the hoax? To make Tokubei send for fifty pieces of gold, of course. It was clever of the man to accuse the shrine priestess of fraud and pretend reluctance to let Tokubei send his message.

143   I couldn't even feel angry toward the man and his daughter— or mother, sister, wife, whatever. He could have killed me and taken my swords, which he clearly admired. Perhaps he was really a ronin and felt sympathetic toward another one.

144   When I returned to the house, Tokubei was looking resigned. "I've decided to send for the whole fifty gold pieces." He sighed.

145   "Don't bother," I said. "In fact we should be leaving as soon as possible. We shouldn't even stop here for a drink, especially not of wine."

146   Tokubei stared. "What do you mean? If I go back home, I'll find everything changed!"

147   "Nothing will be changed," I told him. "Your wife will be as young and beautiful as ever."

148   "I don't understand," he said. "Fifty years..."

149   "It's a joke," I said. "The people here have a peculiar sense of humor, and they've played a joke on us."

150   Tokubei's mouth hung open. Finally he closed it with a snap. He stared at the host, and his face became first red and then purple. "You—you were trying to swindle me!" He turned furiously to me. "And you let them do this!"

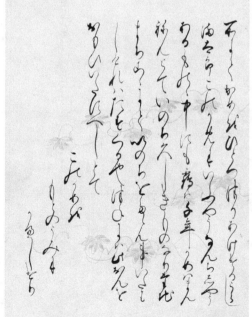

FIRST READ →

Use Reading Skills
Sequence of Events How does this
paragraph signal a shift from the flashback
to the "frame" story?

SECOND READ →

Analyze Literature
Setting Where are Zenta and Matsuzo
staying now?

151   "I'm not letting them," I pointed out. "That's why we're leaving right now."

152   "Are you going to let them get away with this?" demanded Tokubei. "They might try to swindle someone else!"

153   "They only went to this much trouble when they heard of the arrival of a fine fat fish like you," I said. I looked deliberately at the host. "I'm sure they won't be tempted to try the same trick again."

154   "And that's the end of your story?" asked Matsuzo. "You and Tokubei just went away? How did you know the so-called innkeeper wouldn't try the trick on some other luckless traveler?"

155   Zenta shook his head. "I didn't know. I merely guessed that once the trick was exposed, they wouldn't take the chance of trying it again. Of course I thought about revisiting the place to check if the people there were leading an honest life."

156   "Why didn't you?" asked Matsuzo. "Maybe we could go together. You've made me curious about that family now."

157   "Then you can satisfy your curiosity," said Zenta, smiling. He held his cup out for more tea, and the farmer's wife came forward to pour.

158   Only now she used both hands to hold the pot, and for the first time Matsuzo saw her left hand. He gasped. The hand had six fingers.

159   "Who was the old woman?" Zenta asked the farmer's wife.

160   "She was my grandmother," she replied. "Having six fingers is something that runs in my family."

161   At last Matsuzo found his voice. "You mean this is the very house you visited? This is the inn where time was lost?"

162   "Where we thought we lost fifty years," said Zenta. "Perhaps I should have warned you first. But I was almost certain that we'd be safe this time. And I see that I was right."

163   He turned to the woman again. "You and your husband are farmers now, aren't you? What happened to the man who was the host?"

164   "He's dead," she said quietly. "He was my brother, and he was telling you the truth when he said that he was a

ronin. Two years ago he found work with another warlord, but he was killed in battle only a month later."

165   Matsuzo was peering at the pair of sliding doors, which he hadn't noticed before. "I see that you've put up the faded set of paintings. The winter scene is on the left side."

166   The woman nodded. "We sold the newer pair of doors. My husband said that we're farmers now and that people in our position don't need valuable paintings. We used the money to buy some new farm implements."

167   She took up the teapot again. "Would you like another cup of tea?" she asked Matsuzo.

168   Staring at her left hand, Matsuzo had a sudden qualm. "I—I don't think I want any more."

169   Everybody laughed. ✤

FIRST READ

Use Reading Skills
Sequence of Events What happened to their host after Zenta and Tokubei's visit to the inn?

Mirrors & Windows

What if you could sell ten years of your life? What amount, if any, would make it worthwhile to lose the possibilities those years might hold for you? What do you think time is worth?

_____

_____

_____

_____

Find Meaning	Make Judgments
1. (a) What do Zenta and Tokubei notice that is unusual about the girl at the inn? (b) Why do you suppose the girl, and later the old woman, makes no effort to hide her left hand?	**4.** (a) What words, behaviors, and gestures demonstrate Tokubei's attitude about money? (b) How do these attitudes affect his response when he learns about the hoax?
2. (a) While Tokubei and the host are arguing about whether Tokubei should send for money, what does Zenta decide to do, and how does the host respond? (b) Why does a rueful smile appear on the host's lips?	**5.** (a) Why do you think the innkeeper decides to try to swindle the two travelers? (b) Do you think he feels guilty? Explain.
	6. Why do you think Zenta is more forgiving of the innkeeper and his family than Tokubei is?

Analyze Literature

Setting Setting often has an effect on plot. Use a Venn diagram to list the details that describe the inn when Zenta and Tokubei arrive and "after fifty years," when they awaken from their drugged sleep. What details are the same? What details are different? How do these details influence the plot?

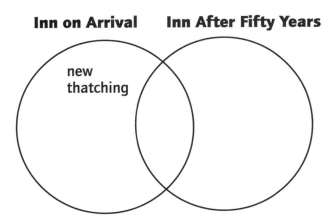

Inn on Arrival   **Inn After Fifty Years**

new thatching

Writing Connection

Informative Writing Consider how Zenta's story would be different if the "frame" story featuring Zenta, Matsuzo, and the farmer's family were removed. Write a short **literary analysis** of "The Inn of Lost Time" in which you examine how the author's use of flashback helps increase suspense. Include a thesis and support.

Unit 2

HOLLYWOOD and the Pits page 96

SHORT STORY by Cherylene Lee

Scientific Context The La Brea Tar Pits are a major tourist attraction in Los Angeles, California. They began to form nearly 40,000 years ago, when the area was home to such animals as saber-toothed cats, ground sloths, and mammoths. The "tar" is really asphalt, which seeps out of petroleum deposits. Animals entered a watering hole and were trapped by tar under the water. The remains of the animals churn in the tar.

Reader's Context How is becoming a teenager like falling into tar? Do parents really remember what growing up is like?

_____

_____

Set Purpose

Before you begin reading, skim the story for unfamiliar terms. Make a list of terms you need to look up.

Use Reading Skills

Analyze Cause and Effect You can keep track of causes and effects in this story by creating a cause-effect chart. As you read, create a cause-effect chart like the one below.

Analyze Literature

Point of View A story's **point of view** reflects the vantage point of the narrator. With the _first-person point of view_, the narrator is part of the action, but with the _third-person point of view_, the narrator observes the action. "Hollywood and the Pits" uses both points of view. As you read, think about how the alternating points of view influence the mood, the plot, and your understanding of the main character.

Cause	Effect
Narrator begins to grow up	

A Short Story by Cherylene Lee

HOLLYWOOD and the Pits

1 1968, when I was fifteen, the pit opened its secret to me. I breathed, ate, slept, dreamed about the La Brea Tar Pits. I spent summer days working the archaeological dig, and in dreams saw the bones glistening, the broken pelvises, the skulls, the vertebrae[1] looped like a woman's pearls hanging on an invisible cord. I welcomed those dreams. I wanted to know where the next skeleton was, identify it, record its position, discover whether it was whole or not. I wanted to know where to dig in the coarse, black, gooey sand. I lost myself there and found something else.

2 My mother thought something was wrong with me. Was it good for a teenager to be fascinated by death? Especially animal death in the Pleistocene?[2] Was it normal to be so **obsessed** by a sticky brown hole in the ground in the center of Los Angeles? I don't know if it was normal or not, but it seemed perfectly logical to me. After all, I grew up in Hollywood, a place where dreams and nightmares can often take the same shape. What else would a child actor do?

3 "Thank you very much, dear. We'll be letting you know."

4 I knew what that meant. It meant I would never hear from them again. I didn't get the job. I heard that phrase a lot that year.

5 I walked out of the plush office, leaving behind the casting director, producer, director, writer, and whoever else came to listen to my reading for a semiregular role on a family sitcom. The carpet made no sound when I opened and shut the door.

6 I passed the other girls waiting in the reception room, each poring over her script. The mothers were waiting in a separate room, chattering about their daughters' latest commercials, interviews, callbacks, jobs. It sounded like every Oriental[3] kid in Hollywood was working except me.

7 My mother used to have a lot to say in those waiting rooms. Ever since I was three, when I started at the Meglin Kiddie Dance Studio, I was **dubbed** "The Chinese Shirley Temple"—always the one to be picked at auditions and inter

---

2. corresponded. Communicated by letter
3. plodder. One who works slowly and monotonously; a drudge

SECOND READ

Analyze Literature
Point of View Is the narrator part of the action? What else can you tell about the narrator so far?

dub (dʉb) *v.,* give a nickname

views, always the one to get the speaking lines, always called "the one-shot kid," because I could do my scenes in one take—even tight close-ups.[4] My mother would only talk about me behind my back because she didn't want me to hear her brag, but I knew that she was proud. In a way I was proud too, though I never dared admit it. I didn't want to be called a showoff. But I didn't exactly know what I did to be proud of either. I only knew that at fifteen I was now being passed over at all these interviews when before I would be chosen.

8 My mother looked at my face hopefully when I came into the room. I gave her a quick shake of the head. She looked bewildered.[5] I felt bad for my mother then. How could I explain it to her? I didn't understand it myself. We left, saying polite good-byes to all the other mothers.

9 We didn't say anything until the studio parking lot, where we had to search for our old blue Chevy among rows and rows of parked cars baking in the Hollywood heat.

10 "How did it go? Did you read clearly? Did you tell them you're available?"

11 "I don't think they care if I'm available or not, Ma."

12 "Didn't you read well? Did you remember to look up so they could see your eyes? Did they ask you if you could play the piano? Did you tell them you could learn?"

13 The **barrage** of questions stopped when we finally spotted our car. I didn't answer her. My mother asked about the piano because I lost out in an audition once to a Chinese girl who already knew how to play.

bar•rage (bə räzh´) *n.*, outpouring of many things at once

14 My mother took off the towel that shielded the steering wheel from the heat. "You're getting to be such a big girl," she said, starting the car in neutral. "But don't worry, there's always next time. You have what it takes. That's special." She put the car into forward and we drove through a parking lot that had an endless number of identical cars all facing the same direction. We drove back home in silence.

15 *In the La Brea Tar Pits many of the excavated bones belong to juvenile[6] mammals. Thousands of years ago thirsty young animals in the area were drawn to watering holes, not knowing they were traps. Those inviting pools had false bottoms made of sticky tar, which immobilized its victims and preserved their bones when they died. Innocence trapped by ignorance. The tar pits record that well.*

---

4. **tight close-ups.** Film shots in which a performer's face fills the camera lens
5. **bewildered.** Puzzled
6. juvenile. Young

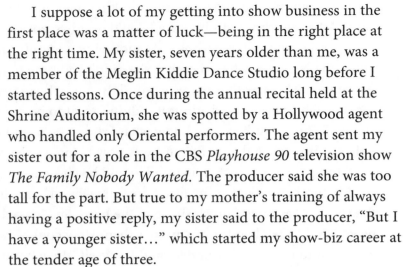

FIRST READ

Use Reading Skills
Analyze Cause and Effect What launched the narrator's Hollywood career?

16   I suppose a lot of my getting into show business in the first place was a matter of luck—being in the right place at the right time. My sister, seven years older than me, was a member of the Meglin Kiddie Dance Studio long before I started lessons. Once during the annual recital held at the Shrine Auditorium, she was spotted by a Hollywood agent who handled only Oriental performers. The agent sent my sister out for a role in the CBS *Playhouse 90* television show *The Family Nobody Wanted.* The producer said she was too tall for the part. But true to my mother's training of always having a positive reply, my sister said to the producer, "But I have a younger sister…" which started my show-biz career at the tender age of three.

17   My sister and I were lucky. We enjoyed singing and dancing, we were natural hams, and our parents never discouraged us. In fact they were our biggest fans. My mother chauffeured us to all our dance lessons, lessons we begged to take. She drove us to interviews, took us to studios, went on location with us, drilled us on our lines, made sure we kept up our schoolwork and didn't sass back the tutors hired by studios to teach us for three hours a day. She never complained about being a stage mother. She said that we made her proud.

18   My father must have felt pride too, because he paid for a choreographer to put together our sister act: "The World Famous Lee Sisters," fifteen minutes of song and dance, real vaudeville[7] stuff. We joked about that a lot, "Yeah, the Lee Sisters—Ug-Lee and Home-Lee," but we definitely had a good time. So did our parents. Our father especially liked our getting booked into Las Vegas at the New Frontier Hotel on the Strip. He liked to gamble there, though he said the craps tables in that hotel were "cold," not like the casinos in downtown Las Vegas, where all the "hot" action took place.

19   In Las Vegas our sister act was part of a show called "Oriental Holiday." The show was about a Hollywood producer going to the Far East, finding undiscovered talent, and bringing it back to the U.S. We did two shows a night in the main showroom, one at eight and one at twelve, and on weekends a third show at two in the morning. It ran the entire

---

7. vaudeville. Theatrical variety show

summer, often to standing-room-only audiences—a thousand people a show.

20   Our sister act worked because of the age and height difference. My sister then was fourteen and nearly five foot two; I was seven and very small for my age—people thought we were cute. We had song-and-dance routines to old tunes like "Ma, He's Making Eyes at Me," "Together," and "I'm Following You," and my father hired a writer to adapt the lyrics to "I Enjoy Being a Girl," which came out "We Enjoy Being Chinese." We also told corny jokes, but the Las Vegas audience seemed to enjoy it. Here we were, two kids, staying up late and jumping around, and getting paid besides. To me the applause sometimes sounded like static, sometimes like distant waves. It always amazed me when people applauded. The owner of the hotel liked us so much, he invited us back to perform in shows for three summers in a row. That was before I grew too tall and the sister act didn't seem so cute anymore.

21   *Many of the skeletons in the tar pits are found incomplete—particularly the skeletons of the young, which have only soft cartilage connecting the bones. In life the soft tissue allows for growth, but in death it dissolves quickly. Thus the skeletons of young animals are more apt to be scattered, especially the vertebrae protecting the spinal cord. In the tar pits, the central ends of many vertebrae are found unconnected to any skeleton. Such bone fragments are shaped like valentines, disks that are slightly lobed—heart-shaped shields that have lost their connection to what they were meant to protect.*

22   I never felt my mother pushed me to do something I didn't want to do. But I always knew if something I did pleased her. She was generous with her praise, and I was sensitive when she withheld it. I didn't like to disappoint her.

23   I took to performing easily, and since I had started out so young, making movies or doing shows didn't feel like anything special. It was part of my childhood—like going to the dentist one morning or going to school the next. I didn't wonder if I wanted a particular role or wanted to be in a show or how I would feel if I didn't get in. Until I was fifteen, it never occurred to me that one day I wouldn't get parts or that I might not "have what it takes."

24   When I was younger, I got a lot of roles because I was so small for my age. When I was nine years old, I could pass

FIRST READ

Make Connections
What does the tone of this writing remind you of? Explain.

for five or six. I was really short. I was always teased about it when I was in elementary school, but I didn't mind because my height got me movie jobs. I could read and memorize lines that actual five-year-olds couldn't. My mother told people she made me sleep in a drawer so I wouldn't grow any bigger.

25 But when I turned fifteen, it was as if my body, which hadn't grown for so many years, suddenly made up for lost time. I grew five inches in seven months. My mother was amazed. Even I couldn't get used to it. I kept knocking into things, my clothes didn't fit right, I felt awkward and clumsy when I moved. Dumb things that I had gotten away with, like paying children's prices at the movies instead of junior admission, I couldn't do anymore. I wasn't a shrimp or a small fry any longer. I was suddenly normal.

26 Before that summer my mother had always claimed she wanted me to be normal. She didn't want me to become spoiled by the attention I received when I was working at the studios. I still had chores to do at home, went to public school when I wasn't working, was punished severely when I behaved badly. She didn't want me to feel I was different just because I was in the movies. When I was eight, I was interviewed by a reporter who wanted to know if I thought I had a big head.

27 "Sure," I said.

28 "No you don't," my mother interrupted, which was really unusual, because she generally never said anything. She wanted me to speak for myself.

29 I didn't understand the question. My sister had always made fun of my head. She said my body was too tiny for the weight—I looked like a walking Tootsie Pop. I thought the reporter was making the same observation.

30 "She better not get that way," my mother said fiercely. "She's not any different from anyone else. She's just lucky and small for her age."

31 The reporter turned to my mother, "Some parents push their children to act. The kids feel like they're used."

32 "I don't do that—I'm not that way," my mother told the reporter.

33 But when she was sitting silently in all those waiting rooms while I was being turned down for one job after another, I could almost feel her wanting to shout, "Use her. Use her. What is wrong with her? Doesn't she have it anymore?" I didn't know what I had had that I didn't seem to have

---

FIRST READ

Make Connections
What feeling do you think the author wants to convey by this comparison to a Tootsie Pop?

FIRST READ

Make Connections
Why might most parents have mixed feelings about whether a child should be "normal"?

anymore. My mother had told the reporter that I was like everyone else. But when my life was like everyone else's, why was she disappointed?

34 *The churning action of the La Brea Tar Pits makes inter-preting the record of past events extremely difficult. The usual order of deposition[8]—the oldest on the bottom, the youngest on the top—loses all meaning when some of the oldest fossils can be brought to the surface by the move-ment of natural gas. One must look for an undisturbed spot, a place untouched by the action of underground springs or natural gas or human interference. Complete skeletons become important, because they indicate areas of least disturbance. But such spots of calm are rare. Whole blocks of the tar pit can become displaced,[9] making false sequences of the past, skewing the interpretation for what is the true order of nature.*

35 That year before my sixteenth birthday, my mother seemed to spend a lot of time looking through my old scrap-books, staring at all the eight-by-ten glossies of the shows that I had done. In the summer we visited with my grandmother often, since I wasn't working and had lots of free time. I would go out to the garden to read or sunbathe, but I could hear my mother and grandmother talking.

36 "She was so cute back then. She worked with Gene Kelly when she was five years old. She was so smart for her age. I don't know what's wrong with her."

37 "She's fifteen."

38 "She's too young to be an ingénue[10] and too old to be cute. The studios forget so quickly. By the time she's old enough to play an ingénue, they won't remember her."

39 "Does she have to work in the movies? Hand me the scissors."

40 My grandmother was making false eyelashes using the hair from her hairbrush. When she was young she had incredible hair. I saw an old photograph of her when it flowed beyond her waist like a cascading black waterfall. At seventy, her hair was still black as night, which made her few strands of silver look like shooting stars. But her hair had thinned greatly with age. It sometimes fell out in clumps. She wore it brushed back

FIRST READ

Use Reading Skills
Analyze Cause and Effect Why does the narrator's mother spend so much time reviewing the past?

---

8. **order of deposition.** Sequence in which layers of sediment are left behind when water flows over an area and then recedes
9. **Whole blocks of the tar pit can become displaced.** Tar is warm enough to flow very slowly, and whole sections can move from one place to another.
10. **ingénue. Inexperienced young woman**

in a bun with a hairpiece for added fullness. My grand-mother had always been proud of her hair, but once she started making false eyelashes from it, she wasn't proud of the way it looked anymore. She said she was proud of it now because it made her useful.

41   It was painstaking work—tying knots into strands of hair, then tying them together to form feathery little crescents. Her glamorous false eyelashes were much sought after. Theatrical makeup artists waited months for her work. But my grand-mother said what she liked was that she was doing something, making a contribution, and besides it didn't cost her anything. No overhead. "Till I go bald," she often joked.

42   She tried to teach me her art that summer, but for some reason strands of my hair wouldn't stay tied in knots.

43   "Too springy," my grandmother said. "Your hair is still too young." And because I was frustrated then, frustrated with everything about my life, she added, "You have to wait until your hair falls out, like mine. Something to look forward to, eh?" She had laughed and patted my hand.

44   My mother was going on and on about my lack of work, what might be wrong, that something she couldn't quite put her finger on. I heard my grandmother reply, but I didn't catch it all: "Movies are just make-believe, not real life. Like what I make with my hair that falls out—false. False eyelashes. Not meant to last."

45   *The remains in the La Brea Tar Pits are mostly of carnivorous animals. Very few herbivores are found—the ratio is five to one, a perversion of the natural food chain.[11] The ratio is easy to explain. Thousands of years ago a thirsty animal sought a drink from the pools of water only to find itself trapped by the bottom, gooey with subterranean oil. A shriek of agony from the trapped victim drew flesh-eating __predators__, which were then trapped themselves by the very same ooze which provided the bait. The cycle repeated itself countless times. The number of victims grew, lured by the image of easy food, the deception of an easy kill. The animals piled on top of one another. For over ten thousand years the promise of the place drew animals of all sorts, mostly predators and __scavengers__—dire wolves,[12] panthers, coyotes, vultures—all hungry for their chance. Most were*

pred·a·tor (pred´ ə tər) *n.,* animal that gets food by capturing and eating other animals

scav·en·ger (scav´ ən jər) *n.,* animal that gets food by eating the dead bodies of other animals

11. **perversion of the natural food chain.** Plant-eaters (herbivores) usually greatly outnumber meat-eaters (carnivores); a perversion reverses this relationship.
12. **dire wolves.** Members of an extinct species of California wolf *(Canis dirus)*

sucked down against their will in those watering holes destined to be called the La Brea Tar Pits in a place to be named the City of Angels, home of Hollywood movie stars.

46   I spent a lot of time by myself that summer, wondering what it was that I didn't have anymore. Could I get it back? How could I if I didn't know what it was?

47   That's when I discovered the La Brea Tar Pits. Hidden behind the County Art Museum on trendy Wilshire Boulevard, I found a job that didn't require me to be small or cute for my age. I didn't have to audition. No one said, "Thank you very much, we'll call you." Or if they did, they meant it. I volunteered my time one afternoon, and my fascination stuck—like tar on the bones of a saber-toothed tiger.

48   My mother didn't understand what had changed me. I didn't understand it myself. But I liked going to the La Brea Tar Pits. It meant I could get really messy and I was doing it with a purpose. I didn't feel awkward there. I could wear old stained pants. I could wear T-shirts with holes in them. I could wear disgustingly filthy sneakers and it was all perfectly justified. It wasn't a costume for a role in a film or a part in a TV sitcom. My mother didn't mind my dressing like that when she knew I was off to the pits. That was okay so long as I didn't track tar back into the house. I started going to the pits every day, and my mother wondered why. She couldn't believe I would rather be groveling in tar than going on auditions or interviews.

49   While my mother wasn't proud of the La Brea Tar Pits (she didn't know or care what a fossil was), she didn't discourage me either. She drove me there, the same way she used to drive me to the studios.

50   "Wouldn't you rather be doing a show in Las Vegas than scrambling around in a pit?" she asked.

51   "I'm not in a show in Las Vegas, Ma. The Lee Sisters are retired." My older sister had married and was starting a family of her own.

CLOSE READ

Use Reading Skills
Analyze Cause and Effect Why are there so many predator and scavenger remains in the tar pits?

Use Reading Skills
Make Inferences How has the narrator's relationship with her mother changed by this point in the plot?

52 "But if you could choose between…"

53 "There isn't a choice."

54 "You really like this tar-pit stuff, or are you just waiting until you can get real work in the movies?"

55 I didn't answer.

56 My mother sighed. "You could do it if you wanted, if you really wanted. You still have what it takes."

57 I didn't know about that. But then, I couldn't explain what drew me to the tar pits either. Maybe it was the bones, finding out what they were, which animal they belonged to, imagining how they got there, how they fell into the trap. I wondered about that a lot.

58 *At the La Brea Tar Pits, everything dug out of the pit is saved—including the sticky sand that covered the bones through the ages. Each bucket of sand is washed, sieved, and examined for pollen grains, insect remains, any evidence of past life. Even the grain size is recorded—the percentage of silt to sand to gravel that reveals the history of deposition, erosion, and disturbance. No single fossil, no one observation, is significant enough to tell the entire story. All the evidence must be weighed before a semblance of truth emerges.*

59 The tar pits had its lessons. I was learning I had to work slowly, become observant, to concentrate. I learned about time in a way that I would never experience—not in hours, days, and months, but in thousands and thousands of years. I imagined what the past must have been like, envisioned Los Angeles as a sweeping basin, perhaps slightly colder and more humid, a time before people and studios arrived. The tar pits recorded a warming trend; the kinds of animals found there reflected the changing climate. The ones unadapted disappeared. No trace of their kind was found in the area. The ones adapted to warmer weather left a record of bones in the pit. Amid that collection of ancient skeletons, surrounded by evidence of death, I was finding a secret preserved over thousands and thousands of years. There was something cruel about natural selection[13] and the survival of the fittest.

Use Reading Skills
Analyze Cause and Effect Why does the narrator prefer the tar pits to a career in show business?

---

13. natural selection. Process in which individuals and groups best adjusted to the environment survive and reproduce

Close Reading

Even those successful individuals that "had what it took" for adaptation still wound up in the pits.

60   I never found out if I had what it took, not the way my mother meant. But I did adapt to the truth: I wasn't a Chinese Shirley Temple any longer, cute and short for my age. I had grown up. Maybe not on a Hollywood movie set, but in the La Brea Tar Pits. ❖

SECOND READ

Use Reading Skills
Analyze Cause and Effect How have the La Brea Tar Pits helped the narrator gain perspective on her life?

Mirrors & Windows

At one point, the narrator says, "I didn't know what I had had that I didn't seem to have anymore." Do you ever feel like you've changed, but people close to you don't seem to notice? Why might this be a common feeling?

_____

_____

_____

_____

Find Meaning	Make Judgments
1. (a) How did the narrator's experiences at auditions change? (b) How well does the narrator understand why her experiences are different?	**3.** (a) What inspired the narrator to volunteer at the La Brea Tar Pits? (b) How did volunteering there change her outlook on life?
2. How does the narrator's mother act toward the narrator?	**4.** (a) What kinds of animals were drawn to the tar pits? (b) How might they resemble people?
	5. Which part of her life do you think the narrator has enjoyed the most? Why?

Analyze Literature

Point of View Summarize how Cherylene Lee's use of both first-person and third-person points of view affects the mood and plot of "Hollywood and the Pits." Make a graphic organizer like this one so you can record your key impressions.

	First-Person Narrator (Hollywood)	Third-Person Narrator (The Pits)
How this influences the plot	**Presents an internal conflict**	**Presents an external conflict**
How this influences the mood		

Writing Connection

Informative Writing How would you describe this story to a friend? Write a three-paragraph **literary response** that describes the conflicts the narrator and her mother experience. Identify each conflict as internal or external and use examples from the story. In your final sentences, tell how the plot resolves each of the conflicts. Make certain you summarize the story in a way that maintains logical order.

THE SCHOLARSHIP JACKET page 108

SHORT STORY by Marta Salinas

Build Background

Cultural Context The term *valedictorian* comes from the Latin *vale dicere*, which means, literally, "to say farewell." The *valedictorian* makes the valedictory speech, which in turn means "a speech of farewell." A valedictorian is not necessarily the top academic achiever. Many people argue that schools should choose a top student for more than academic achievement—for well-rounded combinations of schoolwork, athletic ability, social skills, and creative talents instead.

Reader's Context When have you felt passed over for recognition that you deserved?

_____

_____

Analyze Literature

Theme The **theme** of a story is the main message the author wants to express. To determine the theme, read the story and then think about it for a while. Ask yourself questions such as: Of all the ideas in this story, what could I say in one sentence that would sum up the author's main point? Write your answer in your notebook.

Set Purpose

Based on the title and information in Build Background, predict what this story will be about. Then read to find out how well you predicted the story's theme.

Use Reading Skills

Context Clues Preview the vocabulary words from this selection as they are used below. Try to unlock the meaning of each word using context clues in the sentences.

1. I was so nervous for my interview that I <u>absentmindedly</u> got on the wrong train.

_____

2. Our meeting at the music store was unplanned, a complete <u>coincidence.</u>

_____

3. When he saw the broken glass, his eyes opened wide and his jaw dropped in <u>dismay</u>.

_____

4. Arlis was so <u>withdrawn,</u> she had turned to face the wall and did not respond to the nurse.

_____

A Short Story by Marta Salinas

THE SCHOLARSHIP JACKET

1   The small Texas school that I attended carried out a tradition every year during the eighth grade graduation; a beautiful gold and green jacket, the school colors, was awarded to the class valedictorian, the student who had maintained the highest grades for eight years. The scholarship jacket had a big gold S on the left front side and the winner's name was written in gold letters on the pocket.

2   My oldest sister Rosie had won the jacket a few years back and I fully expected to win also. I was fourteen and in the eighth grade. I had been a straight A student since the first grade, and the last year I had looked forward to owning that jacket. My father was a farm laborer who couldn't earn enough money to feed eight children, so when I was six I was given to my grandparents to raise. We couldn't participate in sports at school because there were registration fees, uniform costs, and trips out of town; so even though we were quite agile and athletic, there would never be a sports school jacket for us. This one, the scholarship jacket, was our only chance.

3   In May, close to graduation, spring fever struck, and no one paid any attention in class; instead we stared out the windows and at each other, wanting to speed up the last few weeks of school. I despaired every time I looked in the mirror. Pencil thin, not a curve anywhere, I was called "Beanpole" and "String Bean" and I knew that's what I looked like. A flat chest, no hips, and a brain, that's what I had. That really isn't much for a fourteen-year-old to work with, I thought, as I **absentmindedly** wandered from my history class to the gym. Another hour of sweating in basketball and displaying my toothpick legs was coming up. Then I remembered my P.E. shorts were still in a bag under my desk where I'd forgotten them. I had to walk all the way back and get them. Coach Thompson was a real bear if anyone wasn't dressed for P.E. She had said I was a good forward and once she even tried to talk Grandma into letting me join the team. Grandma, of course, said no.

SECOND READ

Analyze Literature
Theme Why won't the narrator get a school jacket for sports?

ab•sent•mind•ed•ly
(ab' sənt mīn′ dəd lē) *adv.,* lost in thought; unaware

4   I was almost back at my classroom's door when I heard angry voices and arguing. I stopped. I didn't mean to eavesdrop;[1] I just hesitated, not knowing what to do. I needed those shorts and I was going to be late, but I didn't want to interrupt an argument between my teachers. I recognized the voices: Mr. Schmidt, my history teacher, and Mr. Boone, my math teacher. They seemed to be arguing about me. I couldn't believe it. I still remember the shock that rooted me flat against the wall as if I were trying to blend in with the graffiti written there.

5   "I refuse to do it! I don't care who her father is, her grades don't even begin to compare to Martha's. I won't lie or falsify records. Martha has a straight A plus average and you know it." That was Mr. Schmidt and he sounded very angry. Mr. Boone's voice sounded calm and quiet.

6   "Look, Joann's father is not only on the Board, he owns the only store in town; we could say it was a close tie and—"

7   The pounding in my ears drowned out the rest of the words, only a word here and there filtered through. "... Martha is Mexican....resign....won't do it...." Mr. Schmidt came rushing out, and luckily for me went down the opposite way toward the auditorium, so he didn't see me. Shaking, I waited a few minutes and then went in and grabbed my bag and fled from the room. Mr. Boone looked up when I came in but didn't say anything. To this day I don't remember if I got in trouble in P.E. for being late or how I made it through the rest of the afternoon. I went home very sad and cried into my pillow that night so grandmother wouldn't hear me. It seemed a cruel **coincidence** that I had overheard that conversation.

8   The next day when the principal called me into his office, I knew what it would be about. He looked uncomfortable and unhappy. I decided I wasn't going to make it any easier for him so I looked him straight in the eye. He looked away and fidgeted with the papers on his desk.

9   "Martha," he said, "there's been a change in policy this year regarding the scholarship jacket. As you know, it has always been free." He cleared his throat and continued. "This year the Board decided to charge fifteen dollars—which still won't cover the complete cost of the jacket."

---

1. eavesdrop. Secretly listen to someone else's private conversation

NOTES

FIRST READ

Analyze Literature
Theme What does Mr. Schmidt refuse to do?

co·in·ci·dence (kō in[t]´ sə dən[t]s) *n.*, chance occurrence

SECOND READ

Analyze Literature
Theme How does the narrator know what the principal wants?

dis•may (dis mā′) n., sudden loss of courage; shock

10   I stared at him in shock and a small sound of **dismay** escaped my throat. I hadn't expected this. He still avoided looking in my eyes.

11   "So if you are unable to pay the fifteen dollars for the jacket, it will be given to the next one in line."

12   Standing with all the dignity I could muster,[2] I said, "I'll speak to my grandfather about it, sir, and let you know tomorrow." I cried on the walk home from the bus stop. The dirt road was a quarter of a mile from the highway, so by the time I got home, my eyes were red and puffy.

13   "Where's Grandpa?" I asked Grandma, looking down at the floor so she wouldn't ask me why I'd been crying. She was sewing on a quilt and didn't look up.

14   "I think he's out back working in the bean field."

15   I went outside and looked out at the fields. There he was. I could see him walking between the rows, his body bent over the little plants, hoe in hand. I walked slowly out to him, trying to think how I could best ask him for the money. There was a cool breeze blowing and a sweet smell of mesquite[3] in the air, but I didn't appreciate it. I kicked at a dirt clod. I wanted that jacket so much. It was more than just being a valedictorian and giving a little thank you speech for the jacket on graduation night. It represented eight years of hard work and expectation. I knew I had to be honest with Grandpa; it was my only chance. He saw me and looked up.

16   He waited for me to speak. I cleared my throat nervously and clasped my hands behind my back so he wouldn't see them shaking. "Grandpa, I have a big favor to ask you," I said in Spanish, the only language he knew. He still waited silently. I tried again. "Grandpa, this year the principal said the scholarship jacket is not going to be free. It's going to cost fifteen dollars and I have to take the money in tomorrow, otherwise it'll be given to someone else." The last words came out in an eager rush. Grandpa straightened up tiredly and leaned his chin on the hoe handle. He looked out over the field that was filled with the tiny green bean plants. I waited, desperately hoping he'd say I could have the money.

17   He turned to me and asked quietly, "What does a scholarship jacket mean?"

18   I answered quickly; maybe there was a chance. "It means

SECOND READ

Analyze Literature
Theme Why is being honest the narrator's only chance?

---

2. **muster.** Call forth; collect
3. **mesquite.** Small tree or shrub with sweet pods and fragrant wood

you've earned it by having the highest grades for eight years and that's why they're giving it to you." Too late I realized the significance of my words. Grandpa knew that I understood it was not a matter of money. It wasn't that. He went back to hoeing the weeds that sprang up between the delicate little bean plants. It was a time consuming job; sometimes the small shoots were right next to each other. Finally he spoke again.

19   "Then if you pay for it, Marta,[4] it's not a scholarship jacket, is it? Tell your principal I will not pay the fifteen dollars."

20   I walked back to the house and locked myself in the bathroom for a long time. I was angry with grandfather even though I knew he was right, and I was angry with the Board, whoever they were. Why did they have to change the rules just when it was my turn to win the jacket?

21   It was a very sad and **withdrawn** girl who dragged into the principal's office the next day. This time he did look me in the eyes.

22   "What did your grandfather say?"

23   I sat very straight in my chair.

24   "He said to tell you he won't pay the fifteen dollars."

25   The principal muttered something I couldn't understand under his breath, and walked over to the window. He stood looking out at something outside. He looked bigger than usual when he stood up; he was a tall gaunt[5] man with gray hair, and I watched the back of his head while I waited for him to speak.

26   "Why?" he finally asked. "Your grandfather has the money. Doesn't he own a small bean farm?"

27   I looked at him, forcing my eyes to stay dry. "He said if I had to pay for it, then it wouldn't be a scholarship jacket," I said and stood up to leave. "I guess you'll just have to give it to Joann." I hadn't meant to say that; it had just slipped out. I was almost to the door when he stopped me.

28   "Martha—wait."

29   I turned and looked at him, waiting. What did he want now? I could feel my heart pounding. Something bitter and vile tasting was coming up in my mouth; I was afraid I was going to be sick. I didn't need any sympathy speeches. He sighed loudly and went back to his big desk. He looked at me, biting his lip, as if thinking.

30   "Okay. We'll make an exception in your case. I'll tell the Board, you'll get your jacket."

---

4. **Marta.** The narrator is called *Martha* at school and *Marta* at home.
5. **gaunt.** Very thin and angular

SECOND READ

Analyze Literature
Theme What does it mean that the principal meets her eyes today and not yesterday?

with·drawn (wi<u>th</u> drôn´) *adj.,* introverted; unresponsive

FIRST READ

Use Reading Skills
Context Clues Based on context clues, what does vile mean?

31   I could hardly believe it. I spoke in a trembling rush. "Oh, thank you sir!" Suddenly I felt great. I didn't know about adrenalin[6] in those days, but I knew something was pumping through me, making me feel as tall as the sky. I wanted to yell, jump, run the mile, do something. I ran out so I could cry in the hall where there was no one to see me. At the end of the day, Mr. Schmidt winked at me and said, "I hear you're getting a scholarship jacket this year."

32   His face looked as happy and innocent as a baby's, but I knew better. Without answering I gave him a quick hug and ran to the bus. I cried on the walk home again, but this time because I was so happy. I couldn't wait to tell Grandpa and ran straight to the field. I joined him in the row where he was working and without saying anything I crouched down and started pulling up the weeds with my hands. Grandpa worked alongside me for a few minutes, but he didn't ask what had happened. After I had a little pile of weeds between the rows, I stood up and faced him.

33   "The principal said he's making an exception for me, Grandpa, and I'm getting the jacket after all. That's after I told him what you said."

34   Grandpa didn't say anything, he just gave me a pat on the shoulder and a smile. He pulled out the crumpled red hand-kerchief that he always carried in his back pocket and wiped the sweat off his forehead.

35   "Better go see if your grandmother needs any help with supper."

36   I gave him a big grin. He didn't fool me. I skipped and ran back to the house whistling some silly tune. ❧

---

6. adrenalin. Hormone that gives a person a burst of energy

Mirrors & Windows

When has an older person stepped into a situation to stand up for you? Do you think it's always a good thing, or should adults let young people fend for themselves?

Find Meaning	Make Judgments
1. (a) What does the scholarship jacket reward? (b) Why would the school give it to someone who does not meet the usual criteria?	**4.** Compare Mr. Schmidt and Mr. Boone. Who do you think is the better person? Why?
2. (a) Why can't the narrator participate in sports? (b) Why does the narrator want the scholarship jacket so much?	**5.** Compare the actions of the principal and the narrator's grandfather. Who acts more responsibly? Explain.
3. Which teacher supports the narrator? Why?	**6.** (a) Why does the narrator finally get the scholarship jacket? (b) What does this suggest the theme of the story could be?

Analyze Literature

Theme Review your answers to the During Reading questions on the pages of the "The Scholarship Jacket." Using those responses, make a theme map to determine the story's theme or themes. Draw a large circle labeled "Theme(s)," and then put smaller circles around it. Write details from the story in the smaller circles. Then fill in the center circle.

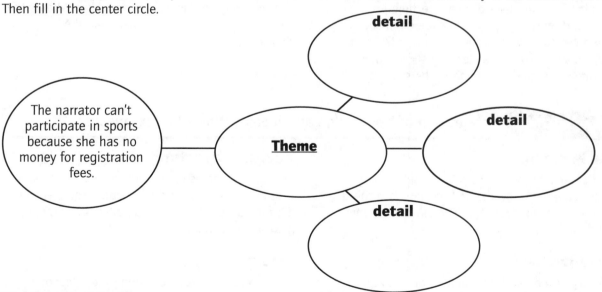

Writing Connection

Informative Writing Imagine you have agreed to read this story aloud to a class of fifth graders. Before you start, help them anticipate the story's overall message. Use your theme map to draft an **informative paragraph** in which you explain the story's theme. Support your explanation with evidence from the story.

Nonfiction Close Reading Model

Key Ideas and Details – What the text says

Build Background

You need to apply two types of background to read a piece of nonfiction effectively. One is the selection's historical, scientific, or cultural context. The other type of background is the personal knowledge you bring to your reading.

Set Purpose

A nonfiction writer writes to inform, describe, persuade, or entertain. Preview the text to decide what you want to get out of the selection.

Make Connections

Notice where connections can be made between the information presented in the selection and your life.

Use Reading Skills

Apply close reading skills such as determining author's purpose and using context clues. Identify a graphic organizer that will help you apply the skill before and while you read.

SECOND READING **Craft and Structure – How the text says it**

Reread

Once you have completed the first reading, it is time to go back and reread sections that you didn't understand.

- **Ask questions** about things that seem significant or interesting.
- **Make inferences,** or educated guesses, about what is not stated directly.

Analyze Literature

A nonfiction writer uses different techniques depending on the type of nonfiction he or she is writing. What literary elements stand out? As you read, consider how these elements affect your enjoyment and understanding of the selection.

Use Text Organization

Determine the structure of the text and how it is organized.

- **Break** the text down or "chunk" the text into smaller sections to check your comprehension.
- **Stop** at the end of paragraphs or sections to summarize what you have read.

Unpack Language

Use context clues, along with the margin definitions and footnotes to unpack the language. What is the effect of the author's vocabulary and the language choices she makes?

THIRD READING **Integration of Knowledge and Ideas – What the text means**

Find Meaning

Recall the important details of the selection, such as the sequence of events and settings. Use this information to **interpret,** or explain, the meaning of the selection.

Make Judgments

- **Analyze** the text by examining details and deciding what they contribute to the meaning.
- **Evaluate** the text by making judgments about how the author creates meaning.

Analyze Literature

Review how the use of literary elements increased your understanding of the selection. For example, did the author use sensory details? How did they help shape meaning?

Extend

Go beyond the text by exploring the selection's ideas through writing or other creative projects.

Unit 3

from **An American Childhood** page 169

MEMOIR   by Annie Dillard

Literary Context Annie Dillard is best known as a nature writer. Her Pulitzer Prize—winning collection of essays, *Pilgrim at Tinker Creek* (1974), follows in the tradition of Henry David Thoreau's *Walden* (1854). In her nature writing, Dillard, like Thoreau, combines vivid descriptions of nature with personal reflections on human nature, philosophy, and spirituality. This memoir describes Dillard's early fascination with nature writing.

Reader's Context What do you remember about your first visit to a library?

_____

_____

Analyze Literature

Autobiography An **autobiography** is a work that describes the life of the author, often chronologically. Autobiographies are written from the first-person point of view, using pronouns such as *I* and *me.* One type of autobiographical writing is the **memoir,** in which a writer recalls experiences of a particular time in his or her life. As you read this selection, notice how Dillard uses details to help the reader share her experiences.

Set Purpose

Preview the first paragraph to predict what the author will reveal about her thoughts, feelings, and actions.

Use Reading Skills

Context Clues Preview the vocabulary words from this selection as they are used in the sentences below. Try to unlock the meaning of each word using the context clues provided in the sentences.

1. The first arrow I shot hit the bull's eye, but my <u>subsequent</u> shots missed.

_____

2. Marta wrinkled her nose at the skunk's <u>noisome</u> odor.

_____

3. It is the <u>prerogative</u> of the coach to decide who plays on the team.

_____

4. John's bad attitude and complaining began to <u>exasperate</u> the others.

_____

5. The <u>tedium</u> of fishing always makes Hank doze off.

_____

A Memoir by Annie Dillard

from

An American Childhood

1   The Homewood Library had graven across its enormous stone facade: FREE TO THE PEOPLE. In the evenings, neighborhood people—the men and women of Homewood—browsed in the library, and brought their children. By day, the two vaulted rooms, the adults' and children's sections, were almost empty. The kind Homewood librarians, after a trial period, had given me a card to the adult section. This was an enormous silent room with marble floors. Nonfiction was on the left.

2   Beside the farthest wall, and under leaded windows set ten feet from the floor, so that no human being could ever see anything from them—next to the wall, and at the farthest remove from the idle librarians at their curved wooden counter, and from the oak bench where my mother waited in her camel's-hair coat chatting with the librarians or reading—stood the last and darkest and most obscure of the tall nonfiction stacks: NEGRO HISTORY and NATURAL HISTORY. It was in Natural History, in the cool darkness of a bottom shelf, that I found The Field Book of Ponds and Streams.

3   The Field Book of Ponds and Streams was a small, blue-bound book printed in fine type on thin paper, like The Book of Common Prayer. Its third chapter explained how to make sweep nets, plankton nets, glassbottomed buckets, and killing jars. It specified how to mount slides, how to label insects on their pins, and how to set up a freshwater aquarium.

4   One was to go into "the field" wearing hip boots and perhaps a head net for mosquitoes. One carried in a "ruck-sack"[1] half a dozen corked test tubes, a smattering of screw-top baby-food jars, a white enamel tray, assorted pipettes[2] and eyedroppers, an artillery of cheesecloth nets, a notebook, a hand lens, perhaps a map, and The Field Book of Ponds and Streams. This field—unlike the fields I had seen, such as the field where Walter Milligan played football—was evidently very well watered, for there one could find, and distinguish among, daphniae, planaria, water pennies, stonefly larvae, dragonfly nymphs, salamander larvae, tadpoles, snakes, and turtles, all of which one could carry home.

---

1. **rucksack.** Knapsack
2. **pipettes.** Small tubes for holding fluid

SECOND READ

Use Reading Skills
Text Organization What kind of organizational pattern does the author use in the first two paragraphs? How effective is this pattern? What do you learn from it?

SECOND READ

Analyze Literature
Autobiography What experience is the author sharing with the reader?

FIRST READ

Use Reading Skills
Context Clues What are *planaria*? What clues in the text help you determine this?

5   That anyone had lived the fine life described in Chapter 3 astonished me. Although the title page indicated quite plainly that one Ann Haven Morgan had written The Field Book of Ponds and Streams, I nevertheless imagined, perhaps from the authority and freedom of it, that the author was a man. It would be good to write him and assure him that someone had found his book, in the dark near the marble floor in the Homewood Library. I would, in the same letter or in a **subsequent** one, ask him a question outside the scope of his book, which was where I personally might find a pond, or a stream. But I did not know how to address such a letter, of course, or how to learn if he was still alive.

6   I was afraid, too, that my letter would disappoint him by betraying my ignorance, which was just beginning to attract my own notice. What, for example, was this **noisome** sounding substance called cheesecloth, and what do scientists do with it? What, when you really got down to it, was enamel? If candy could, notoriously, "eat through enamel," why would anyone make trays out of it? Where—short of robbing a museum— might a fifth-grade student at the Ellis School on Fifth Avenue obtain such a legendary item as a wooden bucket?

7   The Field Book of Ponds and Streams was a shocker from beginning to end. The greatest shock came at the end.

8   When you checked out a book from the Homewood Library, the librarian wrote your number on the book's card and stamped the date on a sheet glued to the book's last page. When I checked out The Field Book of Ponds and Streams for the second time, I noticed the book's card. It was almost full. There were numbers on both sides. My hearty author and I were not alone in the world, after all. With us, and sharing our enthusiasm for dragonfly larvae and single-celled plants were, apparently, many Negro adults. Who were these people? Had they, in Pittsburgh's Homewood section, found ponds? Had they found streams? At home, I read the book again; I studied the drawings; I reread Chapter ³; then I settled in to study the due-date slip. People read this book in every season. Seven or eight people were reading this book every year, even during the war.

9   Every year, I read again The Field Book of Ponds and Streams. Often, when I was in the vicinity, I simply visited it. I

---

3. colophon. Publisher's identifying imprint

FIRST READ

Use Reading Skills
Context Clues The word authority has multiple meanings. Use the surrounding text to identify the meaning of authority as it appears in this context.

sub•se•quent (sʌb´ si kwənt) *adj.*, following in time, order, or place

noi•some (nôi´ səm) *adj.*, offensive smell; objectionable

FIRST READ

Make Connections
How does the admission, at the beginning of this paragraph, that she was afraid affect your feelings about Dillard?

sat on the marble floor and studied the book's card. There was my number. There was the number of someone else who had checked it out more than once. Might I contact this person and cheer him up? For I assumed that, like me, he had found pickings pretty slim in Pittsburgh.

10   The people of Homewood, some of whom live in visible poverty, on crowded streets among burned-out houses—they dreamed of ponds and streams. They were saving to buy microscopes. In their bedrooms they fashioned plankton nets. But their hopes were even more vain than mine, for I was a child, and anything might happen; they were adults, living in Homewood. There was neither pond nor stream on the streetcar routes. The Homewood residents whom I knew had little money and little free time. The marble floor was beginning to chill me. It was not fair.

11   I had been driven into nonfiction against my wishes. I wanted to read fiction, but I had learned to be cautious about it.

12   "When you open a book," the sentimental library posters said, "anything can happen." This was so. A book of fiction was a bomb. It was a land mine you wanted to go off. You wanted it to blow your whole day. Unfortunately, hundreds of thousands of books were duds. They had been rusting out of everyone's way for so long that they no longer worked. There was no way to distinguish the duds from the live mines except to throw yourself at them headlong, one by one.

13   The suggestions of adults were uncertain and incoherent. They gave you Nancy Drew with one hand and Little Women with the other. They mixed good and bad books together because they could not distinguish between them. Any book which contained children, or short adults, or animals, was felt to be a children's book. So also was any book about the sea—as though danger or even fresh air were a child's **prerogative**—or any book by Charles Dickens or Mark Twain. Virtually all British books, actually, were children's books; no one understood children like the British. Suited to female children were love stories set in any century but this one. Consequently one had read, **exasperated** often to fury, Pickwick Papers, Désirée, Wuthering Heights, Lad, a Dog, Gulliver's Travels, Gone With the Wind, Robinson Crusoe, Nordhoff and Hall's Bounty trilogy, Moby-Dick, The Five Little Peppers, Innocents Abroad, Lord Jim, Old Yeller.

pre•rog•a•tive (pri räg´ ət iv) *n.*, special power or privilege

ex•as•per•at•ed (ig zas´ pə rāt´ ed) *adj.*, irritated

14   The fiction stacks at the Homewood Library, their volumes alphabetized by author, baffled me. How could I learn to choose a novel? That I could not easily reach the top two shelves helped limit choices a little. Still, on the lower shelves I saw too many books: Mary Johnson, *Sweet Rocket*; Samuel Johnson, *Rasselas*; James Jones, *From Here to Eternity*. I checked out the last because I had heard of it; it was good. I decided to check out books I had heard of. I had heard of *The Mill on the Floss*. I read it, and it was good. On its binding was printed a figure, a man dancing or running; I had noticed this figure before. Like so many children before and after me, I learned to seek out this logo, the Modern Library colophon.[3]

15   The going was always rocky. I couldn't count on Modern Library the way I could count on, say, *Mad* magazine, which never failed to slay me. *Native Son* was good, *Walden* was pretty good, *The Interpretation of Dreams* was okay, and *The Education of Henry Adams* was awful. *Ulysses*, a very famous book, was also awful. *Confessions* by Augustine, whose title promised so much, was a bust. *Confessions* by Jean-Jacques Rousseau was much better, though it fell apart halfway through.

16   In fact, it was a plain truth that most books fell apart halfway through. They fell apart as their protagonists quit, without any apparent reluctance, like idiots diving voluntarily into buckets, the most interesting part of their lives, and entered upon decades of unrelieved **tedium**. I was forewarned, and would not so bobble my adult life; when things got dull, I would go to sea.

17   *Jude the Obscure* was the type case. It starts out so well. Halfway through, its author forgot how to write. After Jude got married, his life was over, but the book went on for hundreds of pages while he stewed in his own juices. The same thing happened in *The Little Shepherd of Kingdom Come*, which Mother brought me from a fair. It was simply a hazard of reading. Only a heartsick loyalty to the protagonists of the early chapters, to the eager children they had been, kept me reading chronological narratives to their bitter ends. Perhaps later, when I had become an architect, I would enjoy the latter halves of books more.

18   This was the most private and obscure part of life, this Homewood Library; a vaulted marble edifice[4] in a mostly

SECOND READ

Analyze Literature
Autobiography How does Dillard support her claim about "most books"? What realization does she have about her taste in books?

te·di·um (tē′ dē əm) *n.*, boredom

---

4. **edifice.** Large building
5. **infinitude.** Quality of being infinite or without end

decent Negro neighborhood, the silent stacks of which I pondered in deep concentration for many years. There seemed then, happily, to be an infinitude5 of books.

19 I no more expected anyone else on earth to have read a book I had read than I expected someone else to have twirled the same blade of grass. I would never meet those Homewood people who were borrowing The Field Book of Ponds and Streams; the people who read my favorite books were invisible or in hiding, underground. Father occasionally raised his big eyebrows at the title of some volume I was hurrying off with, quite as if he knew what it contained—but I thought he must know of it by hearsay, for none of it seemed to make much difference to him. Books swept me away, one after the other, this way and that; I made endless vows according to their lights, for I believed them. ❧

Mirrors & Windows

What item or experience from your childhood can unlock a treasure trove of memories for you? What kinds of things can people learn from memories of their childhood?

_____

_____

_____

_____

Find Meaning	Make Judgments
1. (a) What information does *The Field Book of Ponds and Streams* contain? (b) Why do you think Dillard is so fascinated by this book?	**4.** (a) What criteria would Dillard use to judge whether or not a book is good? (b) What books would you suggest for Dillard? Explain your answer.
2. (a) What does Dillard notice about the book's card? (b) What is her reaction? (c) Why does she react this way?	**5.** (a) What words would you use to describe how Dillard responds to books? (b) Do you think her responses will change as she gets older? Explain
3. (a) What does Dillard say happens to many books of fiction "halfway through"? (b) What do you think she means by this?	

Analyze Literature

Autobiography How does Annie Dillard help the reader share her experiences? Use a chart to list examples of concrete details and feelings or opinions in *An American Childhood*. Then, in one or two brief paragraphs, summarize the effectiveness of these details, feelings, and opinions in conveying her experiences.

Concrete Details	Feelings/Opinions
The Field Book of Ponds and Streams was printed on thin paper like a prayer book.	reverence; an important book

Writing Connection

Informative Writing An author's voice expresses his or her personality and attitudes. How would you describe Annie Dillard's voice in this passage? Analyze Dillard's voice, or use of language, tone, and sentence structure, in a brief one-page **critical analysis.** Be sure to include a thesis statement and evidence from the text.

Names/Nombres page 193

PERSONAL ESSAY by Julia Alvarez

Build Background

Historical Context Julia Alvarez was raised in the Dominican Republic, a Spanish-speaking island country in the Caribbean. At the time of Alvarez's birth, the Dominican Republic was ruled by a dictator, Rafael Trujillo. Alvarez's father joined the underground movement that attempted to overthrow Trujillo, but the attempt failed, and in 1960 her family fled to New York City.

Reader's Context How would you feel if everyone suddenly started addressing you by a new name?

_____

_____

Analyze Literature

Personal Essay A short nonfiction work that is written to express the writer's thoughts about a single subject is called a **personal essay**. Personal essays are written from the first-person point of view, using pronouns such as _I_ and _we_. Personal essays frequently reveal something about the life of the essay's author and can be written for a variety of purposes.

Set Purpose

Skim the text to look for unfamiliar terms. Identify and define these terms ahead of time to read without interruption..

Use Reading Skills

Identify Author's Purpose Using a graphic organizer can help you determine whether the author's main purpose for writing is to inform, to entertain, or to persuade. Look at the title, skim the selection, and read the footnotes. Then write your observations in the Before Reading section of the chart. Next, read the essay and list the main ideas the author communicates in the During Reading section. Then, in the After Reading section, summarize the author's purpose.

Before Reading	During Reading	After Reading
The author speaks two languages		

A Personal Essay by Julia Alvarez

Names/Nombres

1 When we arrived in New York City, our names changed almost immediately. At Immigration, the officer asked my father, Mister Elbures, if he had anything to declare. My father shook his head no, and we were waved through.

2 I was too afraid we wouldn't be let in if I corrected the man's pronunciation, but I said our name to myself, opening my mouth wide for the organ blast of the a, trilling my tongue for the drumroll of the r, All-vah-rrr-es! How could anyone get Elbures out of that orchestra of sound?

3 At the hotel my mother was Missus Alburest, and I was little girl, as in, "Hey, little girl, stop riding the elevator up and down. It's not a toy."

4 When we moved into our apartment building, the super called my father Mister Alberase, and the neighbors who became mother's friends pronounced her name Jew-lee-ah instead of Hoo-lee-ah. I, her namesake, was known as Hoo-lee-tah at home. But at school I was Judy or Judith, and once an English teacher mistook me for Juliet.

5 It took a while to get used to my new names. I wondered if I shouldn't correct my teachers and new friends. But my mother argued that it didn't matter. "You know what your friend Shakespeare said, 'A rose by any other name would smell as sweet.'" My family had gotten into the habit of calling any famous author "my friend" because I had begun to write poems and stories in English class.

6 By the time I was in high school, I was a popular kid, and it showed in my name. Friends called me Jules or Hey Jude, and once a group of troublemaking friends my mother forbade me to hang out with called me Alcatraz.[1] I was Hoo-lee-tah only to Mami and Papi and uncles and aunts who came over to eat sancocho[2] on Sunday afternoons—old world folk whom I would just as soon go back to where they came from and leave me to pursue whatever mischief I wanted to in America. JUDY ALCATRAZ, the name on the "Wanted" poster would read. Who would ever trace her to me?

---

1. **Alcatraz.** From the mid-1930s to the mid-1960s, a maximum-security prison for America's toughest criminals
2. *sancocho* (san kôˊ chō). Caribbean meat stew (Spanish)

FIRST READ

Make Connections
Why do you think the name *Judy Alcatraz* is so much more appealing to the author than *"Hoo-lee-tah"*?

7 My older sister had the hardest time getting an American name for herself because Mauricia did not translate into English. Ironically, although she had the most foreign-sounding name, she and I were the Americans in the family. We had been born in New York City when our parents had first tried immigration and then gone back "home," too homesick to stay. My mother often told the story of how she almost changed my sister's name in the hospital.

8 After the delivery, Mami and some other new mothers were cooing over their newborn sons and daughters and exchanging names, weights and delivery stories. My mother was embarrassed among the Sallys and Janes, Georges and Johns to reveal the rich, noisy name of Mauricia, so when her turn came to brag, she gave her baby's name as Maureen.

9 "Why'd ya give her an Irish name with so many pretty Spanish names to choose from?" one of the women asked.

10 My mother blushed and admitted her baby's real name to the group. Her mother-in-law had recently died, she apologized, and her husband had insisted that the first daughter be named after his mother, Mauran. My mother thought it the ugliest name she had ever heard, and talked my father into what she believed was an improvement, a combination of Mauran and her own mother's name, Felicia.

11 "Her name is Mao-ree-shee-ah," my mother said to the group of women.

12 "Why, that's a beautiful name," the other mothers cried. "Moor-ee-sha, Moor-ee-sha," she cooed into the pink blanket. Moor-ee-sha it was when we returned to the States eleven years later. Sometimes, American tongues found that mispronunciation tough to say and called her Maria or Marsha or Maudy from her nickname Maury. I pitied her. What an awful name to have to transport across borders!

13 My little sister, Ana, had the easiest time of all. She was plain Anne—that is, only her name was plain, for she turned out to be the pale, blond "American beauty" in the family. The only Hispanic thing about her was the affectionate nicknames her boyfriends sometimes gave her. Anita, or, as one goofy guy used to sing to her to the tune of the banana advertisement, Anita Banana.

---

3. Third World. Developing countries of Latin America, Africa, and Asia

14   Later, during her college years in the late sixties, there was a push to pronounce Third World[3] names correctly. I remember calling her long distance at her group house and a roommate answering.

15   "Can I speak to Ana?" I asked, pronouncing her name the American way.

16   "Ana?" The man's voice hesitated. "Oh! You must mean Ah-nah!"

17   Our first few years in the States, though, **ethnicity** was not yet "in." Those were the blond, blue-eyed, bobby-sock years of junior high and high school before the sixties ushered in peasant blouses, hoop earrings, sarapes.[4] My initial desire to be known by my correct Dominican name faded. I just wanted to be Judy and merge with the Sallys and Janes in my class. But, inevitably, my accent and coloring gave me away. "So where are you from, Judy?"

18   "New York," I told my classmates. After all, I had been born blocks away at Columbia-Presbyterian Hospital.

19   "I mean, originally."

20   "From the Caribbean," I answered vaguely, for if I **specified**, no one was quite sure on what continent our island was located.

21   "Really? I've been to Bermuda. We went last April for spring vacation. I got the worst sunburn! So, are you from Portoriko?"[5]

22   "No," I sighed. "From the Dominican Republic."

23   "Where's that?"

24   "South of Bermuda."

25   They were just being curious, I knew, but I burned with shame whenever they singled me out as a "foreigner," a rare, exotic friend.

26   "Say your name in Spanish, oh, please say it!" I had made mouths drop one day by rattling off my full name, which, according to Dominican custom, included my middle names, Mother's and Father's surnames for four generations back.

---

4. *sarapes* (sə rä´ pēs). Woolen shawls or ponchos (Spanish)
5. Portoriko. Puerto Rico

Use Reading Skills
Author's Purpose Compare the anecdotes about the two sisters' names. What point do you think the author is making?

eth·ni·ci·ty (eth ni´ sə tē) *n.*, belonging to a racial, cultural, or national group

spec·i·fy (spe´ sə fī') *v.*, state explicitly

SECOND READ

Analyze Literature
Personal Essay What does the author want to communicate to the reader about her attitude toward her name?

FIRST READ

Use Reading Skills
Meaning of Words Knowing the meaning of foreign words, such as *madrina* and *comadre,* can be helpful. Identify the meaning and origin of the following foreign words and phrases: *que sera sera, eureka,* and *ad nauseam.*

com·mence·ment (kəm men[t]s´ mənt) *adj.,* graduation

27 "Julia Altagracia María Teresa Álvarez Tavares Perello Espaillat Julia Pérez Rochet González." I pronounced it slowly, a name as **chaotic** with sounds as a Middle Eastern bazaar or market day in a South American village.

28 My Dominican heritage was never more apparent than when my extended family attended school occasions. For my graduation, they all came, the whole lot of aunts and uncles and the many little cousins who snuck in without tickets. They sat in the first row in order to better understand the Americans' fast-spoken English. But how could they listen when they were constantly speaking among themselves in florid-sounding phrases, rococo[6] consonants, rich, rhyming vowels?

29 Introducing them to my friends was a further trial to me. These relatives had such complicated names and there were so many of them, and their relationships to myself were so convoluted. There was my Tía[7] Josefina, who was not really an aunt but a much older cousin. And her daughter, Aida Margarita, who was adopted, una hija de crianza.[8] My uncle of affection, Tío José, brought my madrina[9] Tía Amelia and her comadre[10] Tía Pilar. My friends rarely had more than a "Mom and Dad" to introduce.

30 After the **commencement** ceremony, my family waited outside in the parking lot while my friends and I signed yearbooks with nicknames which recalled our high school good times: "Beans" and "Pepperoni" and "Alcatraz." We hugged and cried and promised to keep in touch.

31 Our goodbyes went on too long. I heard my father's voice calling out across the parking lot, "Hoo-lee-tah! Vámonos!"[11]

32 Back home, my tíos and tías and primas,[12] Mami and Papi, and mis hermanas[13] had a party for me with sancocho and a store-bought pudín,[14] inscribed with Happy Graduation, Julie. There were many gifts—that was a plus to a large family! I got several wallets and a suitcase with my

6. **rococo.** Fancy, flamboyant
7. **Tía** (tē´ ä). Aunt (Spanish); Tío (tē´ ō) is uncle.
8. **una hija de crianza** (ù´ nä ē´ hä de krē än´ sä). An adopted daughter (Spanish)
9. **madrina** (mä drē nä). Godmother (Spanish)
10. **comadre** (kō mä´ drä). Close friend (Spanish)
11. **Vámonos** (vä´ mä nōs'). Let's go (Spanish)
12. **primas** (prē´ mäs'). Cousins (Spanish)
13. **mis hermanas** (mēs är mä´ näs). My sisters (Spanish)
14. **pudín** (pù dēn´). Pudding (Spanish)

initials and a graduation charm from my godmother and money from my uncles. The biggest gift was a portable typewriter from my parents for writing my stories and poems.

33   Someday, the family predicted, my name would be well-known throughout the United States. I laughed to myself, wondering which one I would go by. ❖

SECOND READ

Analyze Literature
Personal Essay How does the conclusion of the essay tie back to the beginning?

Mirrors & Windows

Julia Alvarez, at one point, was willing to change her name to Judy to be more like her classmates. What would you have done in her place? Why do you think people feel the need to fit in?

_____

_____

_____

_____

Close Reading Model

Find Meaning	Make Judgments
1. According to the author, what happens to her family's name at Immigration? (b) Why do you think she repeats the family's name to herself?	**4.** Why does Alvarez say that her older sister's name is "an awful name to have to transport across borders"?
2. (a) What does the author's mother advise about correcting the pronunciation of teachers and new friends? (b) Does she follow her mother's advice? Explain.	**5.** Although the author says she dislikes being considered "exotic" by her classmates, she takes pleasure in "rattling off" her full name for them. What does this reveal about her feelings?
3. (a) Why does Mrs. Alvarez almost change her daughter's name at the hospital? (b) What conflict does this anecdote foreshadow in the author's life?	**6.** (a) Why does the author describe how her family differs from the families of her classmates? (b) Are these differences really important to her? Explain.
	7. (a) What name does the author use when she becomes a professional writer? (b) What does this say about her attitude toward her name?

Analyze Literature

Personal Essay A personal essay is greatly affected by its tone. Tone is the author's attitude toward his or her subject. For example, an author's tone might be humorous, angry, or thoughtful. Use this web to determine the tone of "Names/Nombres." Write details from the essay in the outer ovals. Then write the tone in the center oval.

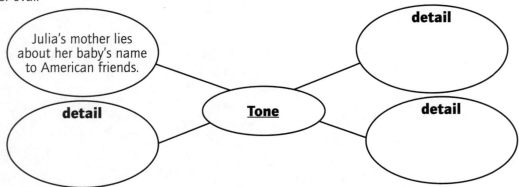

Julia's mother lies about her baby's name to American friends.

detail

detail

Tone

detail

Writing Connection

Informative Writing Is the theme, or central idea, of "Name/Nombres" stated in the essay or is it implied? Write an **informative paragraph** in which you describe the theme. Provide examples from the essay that support your analysis. Share your analysis with the class.

The Eternal Frontier page 202
ARGUMENTATIVE ESSAY by Louis L'Amour

Build Background
Scientific Context When *Apollo 11* landed on the moon in 1969, extensive space exploration seemed within reach. In the 1970s, satellites were put into orbit, space stations were planned and piloted, and robotic missions were launched. In 1984, the year this essay was written, President Reagan announced plans to build an international space station. This meant that funds were going to be concentrated more on the space station than on sending rockets to explore the solar system.

Reader's Context What do you think is the most important frontier today? The most exciting? The most challenging?

_____

_____

Set Purpose
As you read the essay, pay attention to how the author appeals to both your emotions and logic.

Use Reading Skills
Analyze Main Idea and Supporting Details To identify the main idea of "The Eternal Frontier," gather details in a main idea map. Then examine the details to determine the author's overall message.

Analyze Literature
Argumentative Essay In an **argumentative essay,** the author expresses a particular viewpoint and attempts to sway the reader to agree with that position. In addition to presenting logical arguments based on reasons and evidence, an author may use persuasive techniques that rely on faulty reasoning or emotional appeals. As you read "The Eternal Frontier," decide what the author's viewpoint is and evaluate the evidence he provides to support that viewpoint.

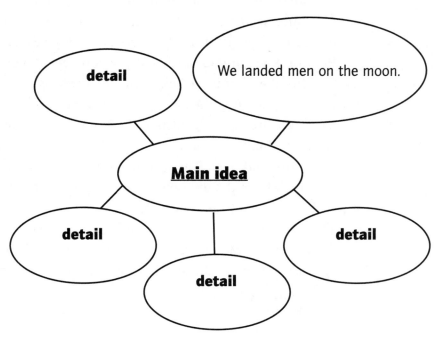

An Argumentative Essay by Louis L'Amour

The Eternal Frontier

1 The answer should be obvious. Our frontier lies in outer space. The moon, the asteroids, the planets, these are mere stepping stones, where we will test ourselves, learn needful lessons, and grow in knowledge before we attempt those frontiers beyond our solar system. Outer space is a frontier without end, the eternal frontier, an everlasting challenge to explorers not [only] of other planets and other solar systems baut also of the mind of man.

pre•lim•i•nar•y (pri li´ mə ner' ē) *adj.*, preparing for the main action or event

2 All that has gone before was **preliminary**. We have been preparing ourselves mentally for what lies ahead. Many problems remain, but if we can avoid a devastating[1] war we shall move with a rapidity scarcely to be believed. In the past seventy years we have developed the automobile, radio, television, transcontinental and transoceanic flight, and the electrification of the country, among a multitude of other such developments. In 1900 there were 144 miles of surfaced road in the United States. Now there are over 3,000,000. Paved roads and the development of the automobile have gone hand in hand, the automobile being civilized man's **antidote** to overpopulation.

an•ti•dote (an´ ti dōt') *n.*, remedy

3 What is needed now is leaders with perspective; we need leadership on a thousand fronts, but they must be men and women who can take the long view and help to shape the outlines of our future. There will always be the nay-sayers,[2] those who cling to our lovely green planet as a baby clings to its mother, but there will be others like those who have taken us this far along the path to a limitless future.

SECOND READ

Analyze Literature
Argumentative Essay How would you paraphrase the argument in this paragraph?

4 We are a people born to the frontier. It has been a part of our thinking, waking, and sleeping since men first landed on this continent. The frontier is the line that separates the known from the unknown wherever it may be, and we have a driving need to see what lies beyond....

5 A few years ago we moved into outer space. We landed men on the moon; we sent a vehicle beyond the limits of the solar system, a vehicle still moving farther and farther into

1. **devastating.** Extremely destructive
2. **nay-sayers.** People who disagree

that limitless distance.[3] If our world were to die tomorrow, that tiny vehicle would go on and on forever, carrying its mighty message to the stars. Out there, someone, sometime, would know that once we existed, that we had the vision and we made the effort. Mankind is not bound by its atmospheric envelope or by its gravitational field, nor is the mind of man bound by any limits at all.

6　　One might ask—why outer space, when so much remains to be done here? If that had been the spirit of man we would still be hunters and food gatherers, growling over the bones of carrion[4] in a cave somewhere. It is our destiny to move out, to accept the challenge, to dare the unknown. It is our destiny to achieve.

7　　Yet we must not forget that along the way to outer space whole industries are springing into being that did not exist before. The computer age has arisen in part from the space effort, which gave great impetus[5] to the development of computing devices. Transistors, chips, integrated circuits, Teflon, new medicines, new ways of treating diseases, new ways of performing operations, all these and a multitude of other developments that enable man to live and to live better are linked to the space effort. Most of these developments have been so **incorporated** into our day-to-day life that they are taken for granted, their origin not considered.

8　　If we are content to live in the past, we have no future. And today is the past. ❧

---

3. **we sent a vehicle...into that limitless distance.** Reference to *Voyager 1*, an unmanned probe launched in 1977 to explore the far reaches of the universe
4. **carrion.** Dead and decaying flesh
5. impetus. Stimulus; force or energy associated with movement

FIRST READ

Use Reading Skills
Analyze Main Idea and Supporting Details What is the author's main point in this paragraph?

FIRST READ

Make Connections
Does L'Amour provide a logical answer to his question? Do you agree with what he says? Explain.

in•cor•po•rate (in kôr′ pə rāt′) v., combine into one body

Mirrors & Windows

Do you agree with L'Amour's viewpoint? Should humanity be trying to explore space? Why do you think exploration has been such a consistent part of human life for so long?

_____

_____

_____

_____

Find Meaning	Make Judgments
1. (a) What does Louis L'Amour think is "today's" frontier? (b) Why does he describe the moon, asteroids, and planets as stepping stones?	**3.** When L'Amour recounts the achievements of the moon landing, how does his use of words, phrases, and repetition reveal his opinion of these efforts?
2. Why does L'Amour include the comparison between the number of paved roads in the United States in 1900 and the number of paved roads now?	**4.** Why does L'Amour include a list of the space program's accomplishments?
	5. L'Amour says, "If we are content to live in the past, we have no future. And today is the past." What does he mean by this statement?

Analyze Literature

Argumentative Essay What is Louis L'Amour's attitude, or bias, about the topic of this essay? Use a chart to list appeals to logic and appeals to emotion that he uses to persuade readers to agree with his viewpoint. Which appeals are most effective? Which are least effective?

"Appeals to Logic"	"Appeals to Emotion"
"The developments of" "the past seventy years show how quickly we can make progress."	"Nay-sayers are like" "babies clinging to their mothers."

Writing Connection

Informative Writing Imagine that you are an editor putting together an anthology, or collection, of essays and articles about space exploration. Write a **literary response** to "The Eternal Frontier" in which you evaluate the overall effectiveness of this essay. Explain why you will or will not include the essay in your collection.

THE SIZE OF THINGS page 250

SCIENTIFIC ESSAY   by Robert Jastrow

Scientific Context This essay deals with the concept of scale — in particular, things so small or so large that scientists must use mathematical formulas to estimate their sizes. Science is forty years advanced from the time Jastrow wrote this essay, but thinking about unimaginable sizes is as challenging today as it was in the 1960s.

Reader's Context Do you ever wonder what you are made of or where the universe ends? Read for some possible answers.

_____

_____

Set Purpose

Preview the essay by skimming it for unfamiliar terms. Skim the words in Preview Vocabulary and the footnotes on each page.

Use Reading Skills

Monitor Comprehension The author's purpose in this essay is to inform you, so try to keep track of new information on each page. You can use a note-taking chart like the one here. Record Jastrow's main ideas in the left-hand column, and use the right-hand column to list ideas and terms you would like to understand more fully. When you are done, try summarizing your notes at the bottom of the chart.

Main ideas	Difficult Ideas and Terms
The electron is very small.	electron microscope

Summary of My Notes:

> **Analyze Literature**
> **Informational Text** An **informational text** is a type of nonfiction whose basic purpose is to inform rather than to entertain or persuade. Among the most common types of informational texts are articles and essays of various kinds. "The Size of Things" is a scientific essay, a type of informational text. As you read, discover what information Jastrow is presenting.

tes•ti•fy (tes´ tə fī') *v.*, make a statement based on personal knowledge or belief; give evidence

SECOND READ

Analyze Literature
Informational Text For whom do you think the author is writing this essay?

con•clu•sive•ly (kən klü´ siv lē) *adv.*, in a way that ends debate or discussion

FIRST READ

Make Connections
Are you convinced that the electron exists, based on this discussion so far? Why or why not?

A Scientific Essay by Robert Jastrow

THE SIZE OF THINGS

1 I once had occasion to **testify** before the United States Senate Space and Aeronautics Committee on the scientific background of the space program; my talk dealt with the manner in which all substances in the universe are assembled out of neutrons, protons, and electrons[1] as the basic building blocks. After I left the chamber a senior NASA official continued with a summary of the major space science achievements of the last year. Apparently my scholarly presentation had perplexed the senators, although they were anxious to understand the concepts I had presented. However, the NASA official's relaxed manner reassured them, and someone asked him: "How big is the electron? How much smaller is it than a speck of dust?" The NASA official correctly replied that the size of an electron is to a dust speck as the dust speck is to the entire earth.

2 The electron is indeed a tiny object. Its diameter is one 10-trillionth of an inch, a million times smaller than can be seen with the best electron microscope.[2] Its weight is correspondingly small; 10,000 trillion electrons make up one ounce. How can we be certain that such a small object exists? No one has ever picked up an electron with a pair of forceps[3] and said, "Here is one." The evidence for its existence is all indirect. During the 150 years from the late eighteenth century to the beginning of the twentieth century a great variety of experiments were carried out on the flow of electricity through liquids and gases. The existence of the electron was not proved **conclusively** by any single one of these experiments. However, the majority of them could be explained most easily if the physicist assumed that the electricity was carried by a stream of small particles, each bearing its own electrical charge. Gradually physicists acquired a feeling, bordering on conviction, that the electron actually exists.

3 The question now was, how large is the electron, and how much electric charge does each electron carry? The clearest answer to this question came from an American physicist,

---

1. **neutrons, protons, and electrons.** Three main particles that make up an atom
2. **electron microscope.** Instrument that uses a beam of electrons to make an enlarged image of a very small object
3. forceps. Tongs

Robert Millikan, who worked on the problem at the University of Chicago in the first decades of the twentieth century. Millikan arranged a device, clever for its simplicity, in which an atomizer[4] created a mist of very fine droplets of oil just above a small hole in the top of a container. A small number of the droplets fell through the hole and slowly drifted to the bottom of the container. Millikan could see the motions of these droplets very clearly by illuminating them from the side with a strong light so that they appeared as bright spots against a dark background. Millikan discovered that some of these droplets carried a few extra electrons, which had been picked up in the atomizing process. By applying an electrical force to the droplets and studying their motions in response to this force, he could <u>deduce</u> the amount of electric charge carried by the electrons on each droplet. This charge turned out to be exceedingly minute.[5] As a demonstration of its minuteness, it takes an electric current equivalent to a flow of one million trillion electrons every second to light a 10-watt bulb. All this happened rather recently in the history of science. Millikan's first accurate measurements were completed in 1914.

4

The tiny electron, and two sister particles, are the building blocks out of which all matter in the world is constructed. The sister particles to the electron are the proton and the neutron. They were discovered even more recently than the electron; the proton was identified in 1920 and the neutron was first discovered in 1932. These two particles are massive[6] in comparison with the electron—1840 times as heavy—but still inconceivably light by ordinary standards. The three particles combine in an amazingly simple way to form the objects we see and feel. A strong force of attraction[7] binds neutrons and protons together to form a dense, compact body called the nucleus, whose size is somewhat less than one-trillionth of an inch. Electrons are attracted to the nucleus and circle around it as the planets circle around the sun, forming a solar system in miniature.[8]

FIRST READ

Use Reading Skills
Monitor Comprehension What did Millikan want to learn through this experiment?

de·duce (di düs´) *v.,* infer

---

4. **atomizer.** Instrument that converts a liquid or solid to a fine mist or dust
5. **minute** (mī nüt´). Very small; tiny; infinitesimal
6. massive. Containing a lot of matter or mass; dense
7. strong **force of attraction.** Particles in the nucleus of an atom stick together due to a force known in Jastrow's day as "the strong force." Today scientists know that the protons and neutrons consist of even smaller particles that stay together because of "the strong interaction."
8. Electrons...forming **a solar system in miniature.** This "planetary model" of the atom was popular in the 1960s. Scientists have found it impossible to determine the path of a single electron, so today they say that electrons form a cloud around the nucleus.

FIRST READ

Use Reading Skills
Monitor Comprehension How is an atom different from a grain of sand?

dif•fuse (di fyüs´) *adj.,* spread out loosely and widely

5   Together the electrons and the nucleus make up the atom.

6   The size of a typical atom is one hundred-millionth of an inch. To get a feeling for the smallness of the atom compared to a macroscopic[9] object, imagine that you can see the individual atoms in a kitchen table, and that each atom is the size of a grain of sand. On this scale of enlargement the table will be 2000 miles long.

7   The comparison of the atom with a grain of sand implies that the atom is a solid object. Actually, the atom consists largely of empty space. Each of the atoms that makes up the surface of a table consists of a number of electrons orbiting around a nucleus. The electrons form a **diffuse** shell around the nucleus, marking the outer boundary of the atom. The size of the atom is 10,000 times as great as the size of the nucleus at the center. If the outer shell of electrons in the atom were the size of the Astrodome that covers the Houston baseball stadium, the nucleus would be a ping-pong ball in the center of the stadium. That is the emptiness of the atom.

8   If most of the atom is empty space, why does a tabletop offer resistance when you push it with your finger? The reason is that the surface of the table consists of a wall of electrons, the electrons belonging to the outermost layer of atoms in the tabletop; the surface of your finger also consists of a wall of

electrons; where they meet, strong forces of electrical repulsion[10] prevent the electrons in your fingertip from pushing past the outermost electrons in the top of the table into the empty space within each atom. An atomic projectile[11] such as a proton, accelerated to high speed in a cyclotron,[12] could easily pass through these electrons, which are, after all, rather light and unable to hurl back a fast-moving object. But it would take more force than the

---

9. **macroscopic.** Visible to the naked eye
10. **strong forces of electrical repulsion.** Like charges repel. If you try to join two bar magnets at their negative poles, for example, the poles will push each other apart.
11. **projectile.** Something forcefully propelled, like a bullet
12. cyclotron. Instrument that accelerates small particles (like electrons) using electric and magnetic fields

pressure of the finger can produce to force them aside and penetrate the inner space of the atom.

9   The concept of the empty atom is a recent development. Isaac Newton described atoms as "solid, massy, hard, impenetrable, moveable particles." Through the nineteenth century, physicists continued to regard them as small, solid objects. Lord Rutherford, the greatest experimental physicist of his time, once said, "I was brought up to look at the atom as a nice hard fellow, red or grey in color, according to taste." At the beginning of the twentieth century, J. J. Thomson, a British physicist and one of the pioneers in the investigation of the structure of matter, believed that the atom was a spherical plum pudding of positive electric charge in which negatively charged electrons were embedded like raisins. No one knew that the mass of the atom, and its positive charge, were concentrated in a small, dense nucleus at the center, and that the electrons circled around this nucleus at a considerable distance. But in 1911 Rutherford, acting on a hunch, instructed his assistant, Hans Geiger, and a graduate student named Marsden, to fire a beam of alpha particles[13] into a bit of thin gold foil. These alpha particles are extremely fast-moving atomic projectiles which should have penetrated the gold foil and emerged from the other side. Most of them did, but Geiger and Marsden found that in a very few cases the alpha particles came out of the foil on the same side they had entered. Rutherford said later, "It was quite the most incredible event that has ever happened to me in my life. It was almost as incredible as if you fired a 15-inch shell at a piece of tissue paper and it came back and hit you."

10   Later Geiger told the story of the occasion on which Rutherford saw the meaning of the experiment. He relates: "One day [in 1911] Rutherford, obviously in the best of spirits, came into my room and told me that he now knew what the atom looked like and how to explain the large deflections[14] of the alpha particles." What had occurred, Rutherford had decided, was that now and then an alpha particle hit a massive object in the foil, which bounced it straight back. He realized that the massive objects must be very small since the alpha particles hit them so rarely. He concluded that most of the

NOTES

SECOND READ

Analyze Literature
Informational Text What was Rutherford trying to express with this comparison?

---

13. **alpha particles.** High-energy particles (radiation) that are ejected from an atomic nucleus at very high speeds
14. **deflections.** Turning or bending of radiation from a straight course

Use Reading Skills
Monitor Comprehension In the phrases "nuclear energy" and "the nuclear era," what does the word *nuclear* mean?

mass of the atom is concentrated in a compact body at its center, which he named the nucleus. Rutherford's discovery opened the door to the nuclear era.

11   Let us continue with the description of the manner in which the universe is assembled out of its basic particles. Atoms are joined together in groups to form molecules, such as water, which consists of two atoms of hydrogen joined to one atom of oxygen. Large numbers of atoms or molecules cemented together form solid matter. There are a trillion trillion atoms in a cubic inch of an ordinary solid substance, which is roughly the same as the number of grains of sand in all the oceans of the earth.

12   The earth itself is an especially large collection of atoms bound together in a ball of rock and iron 8000 miles in diameter,[15] weighing six billion trillion tons. It is one of nine planets, which are bound to the sun by the force of gravity. Together the sun and planets form the solar system. The largest of the planets is Jupiter, whose diameter is 86,000 miles; Mercury, the smallest, is 3100 miles across, one-third the size of the earth, and scarcely larger than the moon. All the planets are dwarfed by the sun, whose diameter is one million miles. The weight of the sun is 700 times greater than the combined weight of the nine planets. Like the atom, the solar system consists of a massive central body—the sun—surrounded by small, light objects—the planets—which revolve about it at great distances.

13   The sun is only one among 200 billion stars that are bound together by gravity into a large cluster of stars called the galaxy. The stars of the galaxy revolve about its center as the planets revolve about the sun. The sun itself participates in this rotating motion, completing one circuit around the galaxy in 250 million years.

14   The galaxy is flattened by its rotating motion into the shape of a disk, whose thickness is roughly one-fiftieth of its diameter. Most of the stars in the galaxy are in this disk, although some are located outside it. A relatively small, spherical cluster of stars, called the nucleus of the galaxy,[16] bulges out of the disk at the center. The entire structure resembles a double sombrero[17] with the galactic nucleus as the

---

15. **diameter.** Length of a straight line through the center of a sphere
16. **nucleus of the galaxy.** Center of a spiral galaxy like the Milky Way
17. double sombrero. The sombrero is a hat with a high crown and a very wide brim. Jastrow is suggesting that the galaxy's shape is like two sombreros placed base to base.

crown and the disk as the brim. The sun is located in the brim of the sombrero about three-fifths of the way out from the center to the edge. When we look into the sky in the direction of the disk we see so many stars that they are not visible as separate points of light, but blend together into a luminous band stretching across the sky. This band is called Milky Way.

15   The stars within the galaxy are separated from one another by an average distance of about 36 trillion miles. In order to avoid the frequent repetition of such awkwardly large numbers, astronomical distances are usually expressed in units of the light year. A light year is defined as the distance covered in one year by a ray of light, which travels at 186,000 miles per second. The distance turns out to be six trillion miles; hence in these units the average distance between stars in the galaxy is five light years, and the diameter of the galaxy is 100,000 light years.

16   In spite of the enormous size of our galaxy, its boundaries do not mark the edge of the observable universe. The 200-inch telescope on Palomar Mountain[18] has within its range no less than 100 billion other galaxies, each comparable to our own in size and containing a similar number of stars. The average distance between these galaxies is one million light years. The extent of the visible universe, as it can be seen in the 200-inch telescope, is 15 billion light years.

17   An analogy will help to clarify the meaning of these enormous distances. Let the sun be the size of an orange; on that scale of sizes the earth is a grain of sand circling in orbit around the sun at a distance of 30 feet; the giant planet Jupiter, 11 times larger than the earth, is a cherry pit revolving at a distance of 200 feet or one city block; Saturn is another cherry pit two blocks from the sun; and Pluto, the outermost planet,[19] is still another sand grain at a distance of ten city blocks from the sun.

18   On the same scale the average distance between the stars is 2000 miles. The sun's nearest neighbor, a star called Alpha Centauri, is 1300 miles away. In the space between the sun and its neighbors there is nothing but a thin distribution of

18. 200-inch telescope on Palomar Mountain. The Hale Telescope on Palomar Mountain near San Diego, California, was the world's largest telescope from 1948 to 1976. It contains a mirror that is 200 inches across.
19. Pluto, the outermost planet. In 2006, astronomers decided that Pluto is not a planet.

SECOND READ

Analyze Literature
Informational Text How does Jastrow help the reader visualize our galaxy?

FIRST READ

Use Reading Skills
Monitor Comprehension Place these in order from smallest to largest: star, planet, atom, galaxy.

Use Reading Strategies
Clarify In the model Jastrow proposes, what fruit represents the sun and other stars?

void (vôid) *n.*, emptiness

hydrogen atoms, forming a vacuum[20] far better than any ever achieved on earth. The galaxy, on this scale, is a cluster of oranges separated by an average distance of 2000 miles, the entire cluster being 20 million miles in diameter.

19   An orange, a few grains of sand some feet away, and then some cherry pits circling slowly around the orange at a distance of a city block. Two thousand miles away is another orange, perhaps with a few specks of planetary matter circling around it. That is the **void** of space. ♣

---

20. **vacuum.** Space without any matter at all

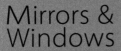

Mirrors & Windows

If you wanted to know more about either atoms or the universe, whom could you ask? Do you think these topics are good for everyone to study, or just for people who are deeply interested in science?

_____

_____

_____

_____

Find Meaning	Make Judgments
1. What does an atom contain?	**4.** (a) Why do you think Jastrow includes information about people and events in history? (b) What did you learn from this information?
2. (a) What makes up most of an atom (in terms of its volume)? (b) How is the structure of the universe like the structure of an atom?	**5.** Jastrow worked as an astronomer, which is a space scientist. Why do you think he spends so much of this essay talking about atoms?
3. (a) Why can't the force of your finger push apart the electrons on the top of a table? (b) How can a proton, which is billions of times smaller than a fingertip, push apart those same electrons?	**6.** Identify several examples of sensory or descriptive detail in this essay. Explain why you think Jastrow's use of these techniques is or is not effective
	7. What kind of text organizational pattern does Jastrow use in the last seven paragraphs of this essay? Why does he use this pattern? What do you learn from it?

Analyze Literature

Informational Text Analyze Jastrow's essay with a K-W-L chart. In the first column, put something you already knew about atoms or space. In the center column, write something you want to learn about that topic. Scan the essay to remind yourself of information the article contains, and then, in the third column, write what you learned from the essay. When you are done, summarize what you learned in a single sentence. As a separate activity, write a full summary of the essay and exchange your summary with a classmate. Write an evaluation of their work based on the accuracy of the main ideas, supporting details, and the overall meaning of the essay.

What I Already Know	What I Want to Learn	What I Learned
That atoms are small and the universe is big		

Writing Connection

Explanatory Writing Jargon is terminology about a specific topic that most people will not understand. Create a **list** of terms from this essay that you believe are jargon. When you have completed your list, draft a definition for each term in your own words. Use a dictionary or other reference material to help you find accurate and complete definitions. Also, using a dictionary, identify the proper syllabication, pronunciation, and part of speech for each word. Finally, consult a thesaurus to identify any alternate word options.

from *The Sibley Guide to Birds* page 262

VISUAL MEDIA   by David Allen Sibley

Build Background

Scientific Context Ornithologists are scientists who study birds, but there are many more birdwatchers than there are ornithologists. Birdwatchers spend hours looking for birds, and they keep careful records of birds they have seen. Birdwatchers use illustrated manuals called *field guides* to help identify birds. In 2000, ornithologist David Allen Sibley published a field guide that describes over eight hundred species of birds in North America. This entry is about one of those species.

Reader's Context Would you know a wild turkey if you saw one? You probably would. Imagine having this kind of book along with you in the woods and encountering a flock of birds. Study this entry to learn more about them.

Analyze Literature

Visual Media In addition to written language, information can be conveyed through **visual media,** pictorial or other graphic forms of communication. There is a wide variety of visual media, including photographs, illustrations, charts, graphs, diagrams, and maps. Field guides, like *The Sibley Guide to Birds,* often contain both text and several different kinds of visual media. As you read this entry, examine how visual media and text interact to provide the reader with information.

Set Purpose

As you read this entry from *The Sibley Guide to Birds,* consider how the author conveys information in words and images. Which do you find more effective?

Use Reading Skills

Draw Conclusions Use details from the entry to draw a conclusion about what traits can be used to distinguish the wild turkey from other birds. As you study the entry, record details with a web. Put details about the wild turkey in the outer ovals.

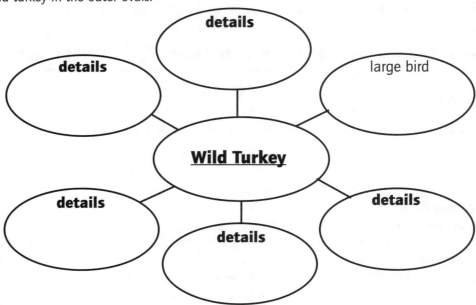

A Visual Media by David Allen Sibley

from *The Sibley Guide to Birds*

WILD TURKEY
One of our largest birds, Wild Turkey is found in flocks in open woods with fields or clearings, usually in oak or beech woods. It is often seen strolling across open ground in flocks of up to 60.

Wild Turkey
Meleagris gallopavo[1]
♂ L 46" WS 64" WT 16.2 lb (7,400 g)[2]
♀ L 37" WS 50" WT 9.2 lb (4,200 g)
Very large and dark, with heavy, dark body incongruously joined to thin neck, small head, and long legs.

Adult ♀[3]
Southwestern

foraging group

barred remiges[4]

all feathers tipped whitish when fresh[5] (compare Eastern)

dark overall

Adult ♀ Southwestern

Adult ♀ Eastern

Adult ♂ Southwestern in display[6]

Adult ♂ Eastern

Voice: Male in display gives familiar descending gobble. Female gives loud, sharp *tuk* and slightly longer, whining *yike, yike* . . . repeated in slow series. Both sexes give a variety of other soft clucks and rolling calls.

---

1. ***Meleagris gallopavo.*** Scientific name for the wild turkey species
2. **L, WS, WT.** Abbreviations for *length, wingspan,* and *weight*
3. **♂♀.** Symbols for male and female
4. **remiges** (rē´ mi jēz'). Flight feathers, which are attached to wing bones
5. all **feathers...when fresh.** A fresh feather replaces a feather lost during molting.
6. **display.** Action of spreading tail and puffing out the chest to attract a mate

---

◀ FIRST READ

Use Reading Skills
Draw Conclusions What does the word *incongruously* suggest about these birds? Use a dictionary if you need help.

◀ SECOND READ

Analyze Literature
Visual Media How can you interpret these drawings to tell a female from a male?

Use Reading Skills
Draw Conclusions What do you think "birds of mixed ancestry" means?

[7] Southwestern populations have tail and uppertail coverts[8] tipped pale buffy or whitish, creating a strikingly different appearance than the darker, rufous-tipped Eastern birds, but the change is broadly clinal.[9] Domestic turkeys, often escaped or released, average heavier than Wild Turkey and have white-tipped tail feathers similar to Southwestern birds. Furthermore, birds of mixed ancestry have been widely introduced, and the species is now found farther north and much farther west than ever before. ♣

---

7. (range map.) The color on this map shows where wild turkeys live in North America.
8. coverts (kə´ vərts). Feathers that help streamline and insulate the bird
9. rufous...clinal. *Rufous* (rü´·fəs) refers to a yellowish-pink to orange color; *clinal* (klīn´ əl) is a characteristic, such as color, that changes gradually, usually in relation to a change in environment

---

Mirrors & Windows

When have you taken the time to closely observe something in nature? How did it affect you? Why do you think people like to watch birds?

_____

_____

_____

Find Meaning	**Make Judgments**
1. (a) What are the two main types of wild turkey? (b) How can you tell the difference between them?	**4.** What elements of the description in this entry would help you most when identifying a wild turkey?
2. Which type of bird gobbles and when?	**5.** (a) How do you think Sibley chose the specific details about wild turkeys that appear in this entry? (b) What kinds of topics or pictures do
3. Reread the paragraph next to the map. (a) What is a domestic turkey? (b) Based on this paragraph, if you encountered a wild turkey in the woods, would you expect it to look exactly like one of these pictures? Why or why not?	**6.** This field guide includes advice on identifying birds. Sibley writes: "The first rule is simple: *Look at the bird.* Don't fumble with a book, because by the time you find the right picture, the bird will most likely be gone....Watch what the bird does, watch it fly away, and only then try to find it in your book." Do you think this is realistic advice? Explain your answer.

David Allen Sibley follows in the footsteps of **John James Audubon** (1785–1851). Son of a French sea captain, Audubon came to the United States in 1803 and began to study and paint birds. He eventually published his work in *Birds of America.* Several years later he published *Ornithological Biographies,* from which this excerpt is drawn.

An Essay by John James Audubon

from **Wild Turkey** page 266

1 While at Henderson, on the Ohio in Kentucky, I had many wild birds. I had a fine male Turkey that I had raised from its youth, having caught it when it was two or three days old. It became so tame that it would follow any person who called it, and it was the favorite of the little village where I lived. Yet it would never roost with the tame Turkeys, but always slept at night on the roof of the house, where it remained until dawn.

When it was two years old, it began to fly to the woods. There it would remain for most of the day, returning home only when night came on. It kept this up until the following spring, when, several times, I saw it fly from its roosting place in the top of a tall cottonwood tree on the banks of the Ohio. There, after resting a while, it would sail to the opposite shore, where the river was nearly half a mile wide, and return towards night.

2 One morning I saw it fly off at a very early hour to the woods. I paid little attention. Several days passed, but the bird did not return. I was going towards some lakes near Green River to shoot when I saw a fine large gobbler cross the path before me and move leisurely along. Turkeys were in the best condition for eating at that season. I ordered Juno, my dog, to chase it and flush[1] it into the air. The dog hurried ahead, and, as it drew near the bird, I saw with great surprise that the Turkey did not run off. Juno was about to seize it, when suddenly she stopped and turned her head towards me. I ran

---

1. flush. Force a bird out of hiding

to them, and you can guess my surprise when I saw that the creature was my own favorite bird, and discovered that it had recognized the dog and would not fly from it, although it would have run off from a strange dog at once.

3   A friend of mine who was looking for a deer he had wounded happened to come along. He put my bird on his saddle in front of him and carried it home for me.

4   The following spring the Turkey was accidentally shot when it was taken for a wild one. It was brought back to me when the hunter saw the red ribbon it wore around its neck.

5   How shall we explain the way my Turkey knew my dog at sight in the woods, after seeing it at home in the yard and grounds? Was it instinct? Reason? Memory? Or the act of an intelligent mind? ✤

TEXT ←TO→ TEXT CONNECTION   Sibley's guide provides a lot of visual information, but it also describes the turkey's behavior and voice. How does Sibley's "Wild Turkey" entry help you visualize the turkey Audubon describes?

_____

_____

_____

_____

Analyze Literature

Visual Media Why do you think Sibley chose to convey some information visually instead of in written form? How might the use of visual media be more effective than language in this context? Create a three-column chart to examine Sibley's use of visual media. In the left column, list examples of illustrations, maps, or symbols. In the middle column, describe the author's purpose for including these. In the right column, briefly describe why this was or was not an effective use of visual media. Finally, write a paragraph that explains the difference between the theme presented in "Wild Turkey" and the author's purpose within "The Sibley Guide to Birds."

Example	Purpose	My Evaluation
illustration of foraging group	useful to bird-watcher in the field; person might actually see this	

Writing Connection

Argumentative Writing Suppose the manager of your local bookstore asks you to recommend some good nature books. Draft a one- or two-paragraph **book review** about *The Sibley Guide to Birds*. Give its purpose and describe any strengths and weaknesses you can name. Then conclude your review by stating whether or not you think the bookstore should carry the book.

Poetry Close Reading Model

Key Ideas and Details – What the text says

Build Background

You need to apply two different types of background to read a poem effectively. One type is the poem's literary and historical context. The other type of background is the personal knowledge and experience you bring to your reading.

Set Purpose

Set Purpose to decide what you want to get out of the poem. Note who the narrator, or speaker, is in the poem.

Make Connections

Notice where connections can be made between the poem and your life or the world outside the poem. What feelings or thoughts do you have while reading the poem?

Use Reading Skills

The **Use Reading Skills** feature will show you skills to help you get the most out of your reading. Apply close reading skills to poetry, such as identifying the main idea and visualizing. Identify a graphic organizer that will help you apply the skill before and while you read.

Craft and Structure – How the text says it

Text Organization

Determine the structure of the poem and how it is organized.

- How are the lines arranged? Do any words rhyme? How many lines are there in each stanza?
- Pay attention to punctuation and line breaks. Chunk the lines in the poem so they make sense.
- Try reading all the way to the end of the sentence rather than stopping at each line break.
- Stop at the end of stanzas or sections to summarize what you have read.

Analyze Literature

What is the purpose of the poem, and what literary elements achieve that purpose? For example, how does imagery or rhyme add to the meaning? Note how these elements affect your understanding of the poem. Poets use different techniques in writing different poems.

Tackle Vocabulary

Look for context clues in the lines near the word, consult a dictionary, or ask someone about words you do not understand. Use the provided definitions and footnotes.

Integration of Knowledge and Ideas – What the text means

Find Meaning

Reread to recall the important details of the poem, such as the images, figurative language, and rhyme scheme. Use this information to interpret, or explain, the poem's meaning.

Make Judgments

- Analyze the poem by examining details and deciding what they contribute to the meaning.
- Evaluate the poem by making judgments about how the author creates meaning.

Analyze Literature

Review how the use of literary elements increases your understanding of the poem. For example, how might figurative language shape a poem's meaning?

Extend

Go beyond the text by exploring the poem's ideas through writing or other creative projects.

Unit 5

Gold page 307

LYRIC POEM by Pat Mora

Build Background

Literary Context Writers who celebrate, in their work, the geography, culture, and traditions of a particular area are known as regional writers. Mexican-American poet Pat Mora is a regional writer who expresses, through her poems and stories, her love of the American Southwest. In the poem "Gold," Mora describes a day in the desert.

Reader's Context Imagine that you are walking in the desert alone. What would you see? What feelings would you have about your surroundings?

Analyze Literature

Imagery The **imagery,** or mental pictures, in a poem often appeal to the reader's senses by describing how things look, sound, feel, taste, or smell. As you read "Gold," think about how the poet uses imagery to help you better visualize the landscape.

_____

_____

Set Purpose

Previewing "Gold" will help you decide how to read and interpret the poem. Look at how the poem is structured, such as the length of the lines and stanzas. Try to determine how these structural elements affect the way in which you read and understand the poem.

Use Reading Skills

Identify Main Idea To identify the main idea of "Gold," gather the details in a main idea map. Then examine the details to determine the overall message the poet wants to convey.

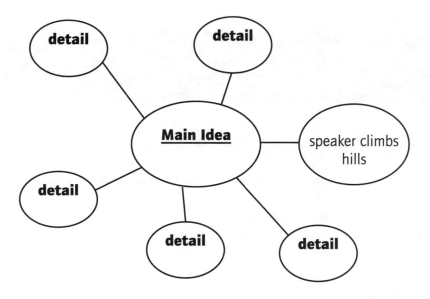

A Lyric Poem by Pat Mora

Gold

When Sun paints the desert
with its gold,
I climb the hills.
Wind runs round boulders, ruffles
5 my hair. I sit on my favorite rock,
lizards for company, a rabbit,
ears stiff in the shade
of a saguaro.[1]
In the wind, we're all
10 eye to eye.

Sparrow on saguaro watches
rabbit watch us in the gold
of sun setting.
Hawk sails on waves of light, sees
15 sparrow, rabbit, lizards, me,
our eyes shining,
watching red and purple sand rivers
stream down the hill.

I stretch my arms wide as the sky
20 like hawk extends her wings
in all the gold light of this, home. ❖

---

1. saguaro (sə gwär´ ə). Large cactus that grows in the southwestern United States and in northern Mexico

SECOND READ

Analyze Literature
Imagery What do the images in this stanza help you see and feel?

FIRST READ

Use Reading Skills
Identify Main Idea What does the third stanza suggest about this poem's main idea?

Mirrors & Windows

The speaker refers to the desert as "home." "Home" might be a place that makes us feel happy, hopeful, alive, and energized. What is a place that you might call "home"? What kinds of things make people feel most at home?

Find Meaning	Make Judgments
1. (a) What is the setting of this poem? (b) What does the fifth line tell you about the speaker's relationship with the setting?	**4.** In line 12, the speaker says the rabbit watches "us." In addition to the speaker, who or what is the rabbit watching?
2. What feeling is conveyed by the speaker's word choice in describing the lizards? Explain.	**5.** (a) What time of day does the second stanza describe? (b) What do you think the speaker is describing in lines 17 and 18?
3. What does the speaker call the setting at the end of the poem?	**6.** (a) List a simile that the speaker uses in the last stanza. (b) How would you describe the feeling that this simile creates?

Analyze Literature

Imagery Think about how the descriptive words and phrases used in the poem help to create images or mental pictures. List these images in the left column of a two-column chart. Then, in the right column of the chart, write about how each image affects you.

Image	Effect
"Wind runs round boulders, ruffles my hair."	This sounds like a friendly wind.

Writing Connection

Informative Writing Write a short **critical analysis** in which you describe the main idea of Mora's poem. Examine the use of images, the setting, the speaker's descriptions, and the poem's tone. In the introduction of your analysis, summarize the poem and state what you believe the main idea to be. Then present evidence in support of your claims.

 page 310

LYRIC POEM   by May Swenson

Build Background

Literary Context May Swenson's poetry is known for its vivid imagery, clever word combinations, and unusual style elements, such as the nontraditional use of capital letters. Swenson once said that poetry is "based in a craving to get through the curtains of things as they appear, to things as they are, and then into the larger, wilder space of things as they are becoming."

Reader's Context Have you ever wanted to be like an animal? What animal?

_____

_____

Set Purpose

Preview the poem, paying attention to its structure; note the length of the lines, the length of the stanzas, and the use of punctuation and capitalization.

Use Reading Skills

Monitor Comprehension Taking notes as you read can help you monitor your comprehension of ideas that are stated in an unusual way. Use a note-taking chart as you read "Feel Like a Bird" to help you understand the meaning of the images that the poet presents.

Analyze Literature

Metaphor and Simile Poets often use figures of speech to compare one thing to another. A **metaphor** is an unstated comparison between two unlike things that does not use the word *like* or *as*. A **simile** is a stated comparison between two things that uses the word *like* or *as*. As you read "Feel Like a Bird," look for examples of metaphor and simile and think about the effects these figures of speech create.

Before Reading Set a purpose.	**During Reading** Take notes.	**After Reading** Reflect on what has been learned.
I am going to determine what the speaker is saying about feeling like a bird.		

A Lyric Poem by May Swenson

Feel Like a Bird

feel like A Bird
understand
he has no hand

instead A Wing
5 close-lapped
mysterious thing

in sleeveless coat
he halves The Air
skipping there
10 like water-licked boat

lands on star-toes
finger-beak in
feather-pocket
finds no Coin

15 in neat head like
seeds in A Quartered
Apple eyes join
sniping at opposites
stereoscope¹ The Scene
20 Before

close to floor **giddy**
no arms to fling
A Third Sail
spreads for calm
25 his tail

SECOND READ

Analyze Literature
Metaphor and Simile What effect is created by the figures of speech used in lines 8–11?

snipe (snīp) *v.*, shoot from a hidden position; direct an attack

gid·dy (gi′ dē) *adj.*, feeling dizzy or unsteady

---

1. stereoscope. Instrument with two eyepieces that presents two photographs of a scene at slightly different angles; the combined image creates the illusion of depth so that the scene appears three-dimensional.

hand better
than A Wing?
to gather A Heap
to count
30 to clasp A Mate?

or leap
lone-free and mount
on muffled shoulders
to span A Fate? ♣

Mirrors & Windows

Poets and artists often gain inspiration from nature. What feelings and emotions do you associate with nature? Why do you think nature can have such a powerful effect on some people?

_____

_____

_____

_____

Find Meaning	Make Judgments
1. (a) In the fifth stanza, what image does the speaker use to describe the bird's eyes? (b) Why do you think Swenson chose this image?	**3.** Why do you think the speaker compares birds and people?
2. (a) What question is the speaker asking in the final two stanzas? (b) How do you think the speaker would answer these questions?	**4.** To what conclusions about birds does the speaker come?

Analyze Literature

Metaphor and Simile How does the poet use metaphor and simile to help you better understand what she is describing? Use the first column of a figurative language chart to list the comparisons you find in the poem. In the second column, write down what is being compared in each example. Then, in the third column, describe what the metaphor or simile helps you envision.

Example of Metaphor or Simile	What is Compared	What I Envision
in sleeveless coat / he halves The Air	wings to a coat without sleeves	a person in a sleeveless coat flapping their arms

Writing Connection

Informative Writing Lyric poetry describes the emotions of a speaker and does not tell a story. Write a one-page **literary response** to explore what makes "Feel Like a Bird" a lyric poem. Consider these questions: What does this poem reveal about the speaker's emotions? How does the speaker interpret or view the bird's behavior? Then share your work in small groups.

Father William page 314

HUMOROUS POEM by Lewis Carroll

Build Background

Historical Context In the 1800s, English schoolchildren were often required to memorize a popular poem by Robert Southey (1774–1843) titled "Old Man's Comforts." In this poem, an old man, Father William, explains that he has good health and a cheerful attitude because he has lived a healthy, virtuous, and moral life. In *Alice's Adventures in Wonderland* (1865), Lewis Carroll poked fun at Southey's poem by having Alice recite "Father William."

Reader's Context How does it feel to be offered bad advice?

_____

_____

Analyze Literature

Rhyme The repetition of sounds at the ends of words is called **rhyme.** *Internal rhyme* is the repetition of sounds within lines. *End rhyme* is the repetition of sounds at the ends of lines. A consistent pattern of end rhymes is called a *rhyme scheme.* Identify the rhyme scheme by assigning a new letter to each new rhyme. As you read "Father William," examine the use of rhyme.

Set Purpose

Read "Father William" to determine how the rhyme contributes to the poem's mood.

Use Reading Skills

Analyze the Effects of Form on Meaning The *form* of a poem involves its structure, meter, and rhyme scheme. The *structure* is the arrangement of lines and stanzas. The *meter* is the regular pattern of stressed and unstressed syllables in each line. *Rhyme* is the repetition of sounds at the ends of words. Create a two-column chart to help you analyze how each of these elements contributes to the meaning and tone of "Father William."

Cause	Effect
Structure: Eight stanzas of four lines each	
Meter:	
Rhyme Scheme:	

Close Reading

A Humorous Poem by Lewis Carroll

Father William

"You are old, Father William," the young man said,
"And your hair has become very white;
And yet you **incessantly** stand on your head—
Do you think, at your age, it is right?"

5 "In my youth," Father William replied to his son,
"I feared it might injure the brain;
But, now that I'm perfectly sure I have none,
Why, I do it again and again."

"You are old," said the youth, "as I mentioned before.
10 And have grown most **uncommonly** fat;
Yet you turned a back-somersault in at the door—
Pray, what is the reason of that?"

"In my youth," said the **sage**, as he shook his gray locks.
"I kept all my limbs very **supple**
15 By the use of this ointment—one shilling[1] the box—
Allow me to sell you a couple?"

"You are old," said the youth, "and your jaws are too weak
For anything tougher than suet;[2]
Yet you finished the goose, with the bones and the beak—
20 Pray, how did you manage to do it?"

"In my youth," said his father, "I took to the law,
And argued each case with my wife;
And the muscular strength, which it gave to my jaw
Has lasted the rest of my life."

---

1. shilling. British coin
2. suet. Fat used in cooking

in•ces•sant•ly (in' se´ s_nt lē) *adv.*, constantly

SECOND READ

Analyze Literature
Rhyme In this stanza, what words rhyme? What is the rhyme scheme?

un•com•mon•ly (ən' kä´ mən lē) *adv.*, amazingly

sage (sāj) *n.*, wise man

sup•ple (su´ pəl) *adj.*, flexible

FIRST READ

Use Reading Skills
Analyze Effects of Form on Meaning How does repetition work to identify the speaker in each stanza for the reader?

25 "You are old," said the youth, "one would hardly suppose
    That your eye was as steady as ever;
Yet you balanced an eel on the end of your nose—
    What made you so awfully clever?"

"I have answered three questions, and that is enough,"
30   Said his father. "Don't give yourself airs!
Do you think I can listen all day to such stuff?
    Be off, or I'll kick you downstairs!" ♣

Mirrors & Windows

How did you respond to the character of Father William? Did you think he was foolish, intelligent, or strange? What people in the world remind you of Father William?

_____

_____

_____

_____

Close Reading

Find Meaning	Make Judgments
1. (a) Who is the speaker in the first stanza? (b) What is surprising about the information he conveys?	**5.** What is unusual about the exchanges between father and son?
2. (a) Who is the speaker in the second stanza? (b) What does he reveal about his personality?	**5.** (a) List some of the comical images in "Father William." (b) Why do you think these images are comical?
3. (a) What explanation does Father William give for the strength of his jaw? (b) What type of explanation is this? Explain.	**6.** (a) In what way does Father William's response to the last question differ from his other responses? (b) Why do you think he responds in this way?

Analyze Literature

Rhyme To describe a rhyme scheme, each rhyme is assigned a different lowercase letter. For example:

Jack be nimble	*a*
Jack be quick	*b*
Jack jump over	*c*
The candlestick	*b*

The rhyme scheme of these lines is *abcb*. Review "Father William," and determine the rhyme scheme of each stanza. On a separate sheet of paper, write out the rhyme scheme. Then discuss how the rhyme scheme affects the mood of the poem.

Writing Connection

Descriptive Writing Use the poem to write a **character sketch** of Father William. Include details from the poem and at least one direct quotation to support your claims about Father William's character. In your conclusion, be sure to sum up Father William's character in a sentence or two. Then compare your sketch with a partner's sketch.

Theme in Yellow page 362

LYRIC POEM   by Carl Sandburg

Literary Context "Theme in Yellow" was published in 1916 in *Chicago Poems,* Sandburg's first major collection. Some considered his approach to poetry shocking; others found it refreshing. Most of Sandburg's poems are in the free verse form and use the everyday language of working people. His powerful voice celebrates the raw beauty of industrialism as well as America's landscape, music, and culture.

Reader's Context What is autumn like in your part of the country? What words would you use to describe it?

_____

_____

Analyze Literature

Speaker The **speaker** is the voice that speaks, or narrates, a poem. The speaker may or may not be the author. Poets often create characters in their poems. As you read "Theme in Yellow," try to determine who the speaker is. Is it a character in the poem, or is the speaker narrating from the outside?

Set Purpose

Examine the poet's use of imagery. Ask yourself questions like "How does this image make me feel?" and "What big idea might this stand for?"

Use Reading Skills

Identify Multiple Levels of Meaning In poetry, writers frequently use images, metaphors, similes, and sound devices to create multiple levels of meaning. By reading and rereading, you can better understand how these different levels affect each other and contribute to the poem's overall meaning. Use a chart like the one below to help you identify and analyze the effects of these different levels of meaning.

Image	golden cornfields at dusk
Figurative Language	
Characters, Setting	

A Lyric Poem by Carl Sandburg

Theme in Yellow

I spot the hills
With yellow balls in autumn.
I light the prairie cornfields
Orange and **tawny** gold clusters
5   And I am called pumpkins.
On the last of October
When **dusk** is fallen
Children join hands
And circle round me
10 Singing ghost songs
And love to the harvest moon;
I am a jack-o'-lantern
With terrible teeth
And the children know
15 I am fooling. ❖

SECOND READ

Analyze Literature
Speaker Is this poem's speaker the author? Confirm or modify your answer as you read.

taw•ny (tä´ nē) *adj.*, warm sandy color

dusk (dʉsk) *n.,* darker stage of twilight

FIRST READ

Use Reading Skills
Identify Multiple Levels of Meaning What do the final four lines suggest about the speaker?

Mirrors & Windows

What do you like most about autumn? What do you like least about it? In what ways is autumn different from all the other seasons?

_____

_____

_____

_____

Find Meaning	Make Judgments
1. (a) Who or what is this poem's speaker? (b) How does the speaker change by the end of the poem?	**3.** (a) What does the speaker claim the children know? (b) In what ways do their actions support this claim
2. (a) What colors does the speaker mention in the poem? (b) Why might these colors be the most appropriate for this poem?	**4.** How was the content of this poem surprising? Explain your answer.

Analyze Literature

Speaker In poetry a speaker can be a person, place, or thing and may or may not express the thoughts of the poet. Use a web to determine the attitudes of the speaker. In the center oval, name the speaker. In each outer oval, write a detail that suggests a characteristic of the speaker. Then write a sentence describing the speaker's personality.

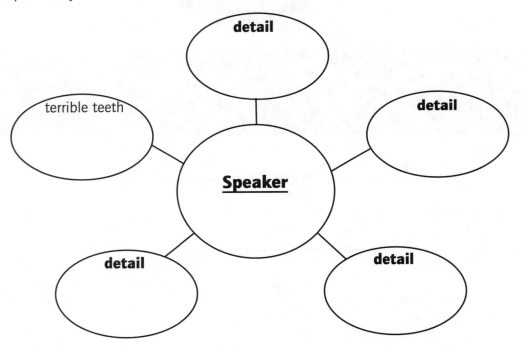

Writing Connection

Informative Writing Think about your reaction to "Theme in Yellow." How does it make you feel? Mood is the feeling or emotion that a writer creates in a work. List some words or phrases that describe the mood of the poem. Consider the speaker's choice of words and images, as well as the speaker's appearance. In a one-page **literary response,** analyze how the speaker affects the mood of "Theme in Yellow."

Once by the Pacific page 367

LYRIC POEM by Robert Frost

Build Background

Literary Context At a time when poets were moving toward free verse and themes of social upheaval, industrial life, and scientific discovery, Frost wrote using traditional poetic forms. He addressed themes of personal relationships, rural life, and nature. Even so, Frost's perspective was that of a modern man. He used simple language in well-crafted lines to express his frequently dark, ironic perspective on nature and society.

Reader's Context When have you ever experienced, firsthand, the fury of nature? In what ways can nature be both creative and destructive?

Analyze Literature

Symbolism A **symbol** is a thing that represents itself and something else. As you read "Once by the Pacific," think about the various things being described. What might those things, including the setting, the characters, and their actions, represent?

Set Purpose

Before you begin to read "Once by the Pacific," answer these questions: How many lines are in the poem? How many stanzas? What is the rhyme scheme?

Use Reading Skills

Analyze Text Organization A *sonnet* is one of the most common poetic forms. A traditional Shakespearean, or English, sonnet is made up of one stanza with fourteen lines organized in three quatrains, or four-line sections, plus a final couplet, or two-line section. The rhyme scheme is *abab cdcd efef gg*. As you read "Once by the Pacific," use a two-column chart to determine how the poem's organization compares with that of a traditional sonnet.

Traditional Sonnet	"Once by the Pacific"
Number of lines:	**Number of lines:**
Rhyme scheme:	**Rhyme scheme:**
Stanza structure:	**Stanza structure:**

A Lyric Poem by Robert Frost

Once by the Pacific

din (din) *n.*, loud noise

The shattered water made a misty **din**.
Great waves looked over others coming in,
And thought of doing something to the shore
That water never did to land before.

5 The clouds were low and hairy in the skies,
Like locks blown forward in the gleam of eyes.
You could not tell, and yet it looked as if
The shore was lucky in being backed by cliff,
The cliff in being backed by continent;

10 It looked as if a night of dark **intent**
Was coming, and not only a night, an age.
Someone had better be prepared for rage.
There would be more than ocean-water broken
Before God's last *Put out the Light* was spoken. ❧

SECOND READ

Analyze Literature
Symbolism What might the waves symbolize? Explain.

in•tent (in tent´) *n.*, purpose

FIRST READ

Use Reading Skills
Text Organization What is this poem's rhyme scheme?

Mirrors & Windows

Would you want to witness the scene being described by the poem's speaker? Why might this scene seem frightening to some people?

_____

_____

_____

_____

Find Meaning	Make Judgments
1. (a) According to the speaker, what are the waves doing? (b) What mood does the speaker's description of the waves create?	**3.** (a) What image is suggested by the personification in lines 5 and 6? (b) What traits does this image seem to convey? Explain.
2. (a) What does the speaker say is coming? (b) What evidence does the speaker offer in support of this prediction?	**4.** (a) How does the last couplet refer back to the beginning of the poem? (b) What do the words *"Put out the Light"* suggest?

Analyze Literature

Symbolism How does Frost use symbolism to convey meaning in this poem? Analyze symbols in the poem by listing the symbols in the left column. Then in the right column, write the meaning of the symbols or the ideas that they suggest to you.

Symbol	Meaning
water	

Writing Connection

Informative Writing Reread Frost's poem. Try to determine, based on the setting, tone, mood, and other details, what caused the speaker to adopt the perspective in the poem. Write a brief **cause-and-effect essay** in which you state the speaker's outlook and determine the causes for that outlook. Use both direct quotations and paraphrases in support of your claims. At the end of your essay, restate your main idea.

Drama Close Reading Model

FIRST READING Key Ideas and Details – What the text says

Build Background

You need to apply two types of background to read a drama effectively. One type is the drama's literary and historical context. The other type of background is the personal knowledge and experience you bring to your reading.

Set Purpose

A playwright presents characters and scenes to say something about life. Set your reading purpose to decide what you want to get out of the drama.

Make Connections

Notice where connections can be made between the drama and your life or the world outside the drama. What feelings or thoughts do you have while reading the drama?

Use Reading Skills

Apply close reading skills such as drawing conclusions and summarizing. Identify a graphic organizer that will help you apply the skill before and while you read.

SECOND READING Craft and Structure – How the text says it

Use Text Organization

Plays are usually divided into acts and scenes, with each scene change indicating a variation of time or place. Stop at the end of scenes or acts and summarize the action that takes place.

What do you learn about the setting, characters, and plot through dialogue spoken by the actors, their actions, or details in the stage directions? As you read, gather more clues to confirm or adjust your predictions.

Analyze Literature

A playwright uses literary techniques, such as plot and dialogue, to create meaning. What literary elements stand out? Are the characters vivid and interesting? Is there a strong central conflict? As you read, consider how these elements affect your enjoyment and understanding of the drama.

Unpack Vocabulary

What is the effect of the author's vocabulary and the language choices he makes? Make sure to use the context clues, definitions, and footnotes to help you unpack the language.

THIRD READING Integration of Knowledge and Ideas – What the text means

Find Meaning

Reread to recall the important details of the drama, such as the sequence of events and characters' names. Use this information to interpret, or explain, the meaning of the drama.

Make Judgments

- Analyze the text by examining details and deciding what they contribute to the meaning.
- Evaluate the text by making judgments about how the author creates meaning.

Analyze Literature

Review how the use of literary elements increases your understanding of the story. For example, if the author uses monologue, how does it help to shape the drama's meaning?

Extend Understanding

Go beyond the text by exploring the drama's ideas through writing or other creative projects.

Close Reading

Unit 7

A Defenseless Creature page 417

DRAMA by Neil Simon based on a story by Anton Chekhov

Build Background

Literary Context "A Defenseless Creature" is from a play entitled *The Good Doctor* by Neil Simon. *The Good Doctor* consists of a series of vignettes adapted from stories written by Russian author Anton Chekhov. Born in 1860, Chekhov began writing comic sketches for humorous journals to support his family and himself as he studied medicine. By 1888, his stories had achieved great popularity. Chekhov went on to become one of Russia's greatest playwrights and was influential in developing the modern short story.

Reader's Context How can persistence convince people to help you even if your request is unreasonable?

Analyze Literature

Drama A story intended to be performed by actors for an audience is called a **drama**, or play. A dramatic script usually includes a cast of characters, a description of the setting, dialogue, and stage directions. As you read "A Defenseless Creature" identify details in the dialogue and stage directions that provide information about the characters.

Set Purpose

Skim the stage directions in *italic type.* What do you think the mood of the play will be?

Use Reading Skills

Identify Cause and Effect As you read a dramatic script, identify cause-and-effect relationships created by stage directions, dialogue, and characters' actions. Determine the reasons, or *causes,* something exists or occurs, as well as the results, or *effects.* Record your ideas in a chart.

Cause	Effect
Kistunov is suffering from gout.	Loud noises bother him.

Drama by Neil Simon based on a srory by Anton Chekhov

A Defenseless Creature

The lights come up on the office of a bank official, KISTUNOV.
*He enters on a crutch; his right foot is heavily encased in
bandages, swelling it to three times its normal size. He suffers
from the gout[1] and is very careful of any mishap which would
only intensify his pain. He makes it to his desk and sits. An*
ASSISTANT, *rather harried,[2] enters.*

SECOND READ

Analyze Literature
Drama What do the stage directions
demonstrate about Kistunov?

ASSISTANT. [*With volume.*] Good morning, Mr. Kistunov!

KISTUNOV. Shhh! Please....Please lower your voice.

ASSISTANT. [*Whispers.*] I'm sorry, sir.

KISTUNOV. It's just that my gout is acting up again and my
5 nerves are like little firecrackers. The least little friction can set
them off.

ASSISTANT. It must be very painful, sir.

KISTUNOV. Combing my hair this morning was agony.

ASSISTANT. Mr. Kistunov.

10 KISTUNOV. What is it, Pochatkin?

ASSISTANT. There's a woman who insists on seeing you. We
can't make head or tail out of her story, but she insists on
seeing the directing manager. Perhaps if you're not well—

KISTUNOV. No, no. The business of the bank comes before my
15 minor physical ailments. Show her in, please...quietly. [*The*
ASSISTANT *tiptoes out. A* WOMAN *enters. She is in her late
forties, poorly dressed. She is of the working class. She crosses to
the desk, a forlorn look on her face. She twists her bag
nervously.*] Good morning, madame. Forgive me for not
20 standing, but I am somewhat **incapacitated**. Please sit down.

WOMAN. Thank you.

She sits.

KISTUNOV. Now, what can I do for you?

WOMAN. You can help me, sir. I pray to God you can help. No
25 one else in this world seems to care....

FIRST READ

Use Reading Skills
Identify Cause and Effect What causes
Kistunov to see the woman?

in•ca•pac•i•tat•ed (in′ kə pa′ sə
tāt′ ed) *adj.,* unable to engage in normal
activities; disabled

---

1. **gout.** Condition that causes painful swelling of the joints, especially of the feet and hands
2. **harried.** Overwhelmed by problems

She begins to cry, which in turn becomes a wail—the kind of wail that melts the spine of strong men. KISTUNOV *winces and grits his teeth in pain as he grips the arms of his chair.*

KISTUNOV. Calm yourself, madame. I beg of you. Please calm yourself.

WOMAN. I'm sorry. [*She tries to calm down.*]

30 **KISTUNOV.** I'm sure we can sort it all out if we approach the problem sensibly and quietly....Now, what exactly is the trouble?

WOMAN. Well, sir....It's my husband. Collegiate Assessor[3] Schukin.He's been sick for five months....Five agonizing months.

35 **KISTUNOV.** I know the horrors of illness and can sympathize with you, madame. What's the nature of his illness?

WOMAN. It's a nervous disorder. Everything grates on his nerves. If you so much as touch him he'll scream out— [*And without warning, she screams a loud bloodcurdling scream that*
40 *sends* KISTUNOV *almost out of his seat.*] How or why he got it, nobody knows.

KISTUNOV. [*Trying to regain his __composure__.*] I have an inkling....Please go on, a little less descriptively, if possible.

WOMAN. Well, while the poor man was lying in bed—

45 **KISTUNOV.** [*Braces himself.*] You're not going to scream again, are you?

WOMAN. Not that I don't have cause....While he was lying in bed these five months, recuperating, he was dismissed from his job—for no reason at all.

50 **KISTUNOV.** That's a pity, certainly, but I don't quite see the connection with our bank, madame.

WOMAN. You don't know how I suffered during his illness. I nursed him from morning till night. Doctored him from night till morning. Besides cleaning my house, taking care of my
55 children, feeding our dog, our cat, our goat, my sister's bird, who was sick....

KISTUNOV. The bird was sick?

WOMAN. My sister! She gets dizzy spells. She's been dizzy a month now. And she's getting dizzier every day.

---

3. Collegiate Assessor. Civil service rank in Imperial Russia

Use Reading Skills
Identify Cause and Effect What does Kistunov think causes the husband's nervous disorder?

com・po・sure (kəm pō´ zhər) *n.,* calmness of mind or appearance

60 **KISTUNOV.** Extraordinary. However—

WOMAN. I had to take care of her children and her house and her cat and her goat, and then her bird bit one of my children, and so our cat bit her bird, so my oldest daughter, the one with the broken arm, drowned my sister's cat, and now my sister
65 wants my goat in exchange, or else she says she'll either drown my cat or break my oldest daughter's other arm—

KISTUNOV. Yes, well, you've certainly had your pack of troubles, haven't you? But I don't quite see—

WOMAN. And then, I went to get my husband's pay, they
70 deducted twenty-four rubles[4] and thirty-six kopecks.[5] For what? I asked. Because, they said, he borrowed it from the employees' fund. But that's impossible. He could never borrow without my approval. I'd break his arm….Not while he was
75 sick, of course….I don't have the strength. I'm not well myself, sir. I have this racking cough that's a terrible thing to hear—

She coughs rackingly[6]—*so rackingly that* KISTUNOV *is about to crack.*

KISTUNOV. I can well understand why your husband took five months to recuperate. But what is it you want from me, madame?

WOMAN. What rightfully belongs to my husband—his twenty-
80 four rubles and thirty-six kopecks. They won't give it to me because I'm a woman, weak and defenseless. Some of them have laughed in my face, sir….Laughed! [*She laughs loud and painfully.* KISTUNOV *clenches*[7] *everything.*] Where's the humor I wonder, in a poor, defenseless creature like myself?

She sobs.

85 **KISTUNOV.** None….I see none at all. However, madame, I don't wish to be unkind, but I'm afraid you've come to the wrong place. Your **petition**, no matter how justified, has nothing to do with us. You'll have to go to the agency where your husband was employed.

90 **WOMAN.** What do you mean? I've been to *five* agencies already and none of them will even listen to my petition. I'm about to lose my mind. The hair is coming out of my head. [*She pulls*

pe•ti•tion (pə ti´ shən) *n.,* formal request

---

4. **rubles.** Units of Russian money
5. **kopecks.** Hundredths of a ruble
6. **rackingly.** With heaves of painful effort
7. **clenches.** Holds or grips tightly

OUT *a handful.*] Look at my hair. By the fistful. [*She throws a fistful on his desk.*] Don't tell me to go to another agency!

95 **KISTUNOV.** [***Delicately*** *and disgustedly, he picks up her fistful of hair and hands it back to her. She sticks it back in her hair.*] Please, madame, keep your hair in its proper place. Now listen to me carefully. This-is-a-bank. A bank! We're in the banking business. We bank money. Funds that are brought here are

100 banked by us. Do you understand what I'm saying?

WOMAN. What are you saying?

KISTUNOV. I'm saying that I can't help you.

WOMAN. Are you saying you can't help me?

KISTUNOV. [*Sighs deeply.*] I'm trying. I don't think I'm making

105 headway.

WOMAN. Are you saying you won't believe my husband is sick? Here! Here is a doctor's certificate. [*She puts it on the desk and pounds it.*] There's the proof. Do you still doubt that my husband is suffering from a nervous disorder?

110 **KISTUNOV.** Not only do I not doubt it, I would swear to it.

WOMAN. Look at it! You didn't look at it!

KISTUNOV. It's really not necessary. I know full well how your husband must be suffering.

WOMAN. What's the point in a doctor's certificate if you don't

115 look at it?! LOOK AT IT!

KISTUNOV. [*Frightened, quickly looks at it.*] Oh, yes….I see your husband is sick. It's right here on the doctor's certificate. Well, you certainly have a good case, madame, but I'm afraid

120 *you've still come to the wrong place.* [*Getting perplexed.*] I'm getting excited.

WOMAN. [*Stares at him.*] You lied to me. I took you as a man of your word and you lied to me.

KISTUNOV. I? LIE? WHEN?

125 **WOMAN.** [*Snatches the certificate.*] When you said you read the doctor's certificate. You couldn't have. You couldn't have read the description of my husband's illness without seeing he was fired unjustly. [*She puts the certificate back on the desk.*] Don't take advantage of me just because I'm a weak, defenseless

130 woman. Do me the simple courtesy of reading the doctor's certificate. That's all I ask. Read it, and then I'll go.

del•i•cate•ly (del´ i kət lē) *adv.*, carefully; cautiously

SECOND READ

Analyze Literature
Drama How do the stage directions in this dialogue contribute to the play's mood?

KISTUNOV. But I read it! What's the point in reading something twice when I've already read it once?

WOMAN. You didn't read it carefully.

KISTUNOV. I read it in detail!

135 **WOMAN.** Then you read it too fast. Read it slower.

KISTUNOV. I don't have to read it slower. I'm a fast reader.

WOMAN. Maybe you didn't absorb it. Let it sink in this time.

KISTUNOV. [*Almost apoplectic.*[8]] I absorbed it! It sank in! I could pass a test on what's written here, but it doesn't make 140 any difference because it has nothing to do with our bank!

WOMAN. [*She throws herself on him from behind.*] Did you read the part where it says he has a nervous disorder? Read that part again and see if I'm wrong.

KISTUNOV. THAT PART? OH, YES! I SEE YOUR HUSBAND 145 HAS A NERVOUS DISORDER. MY, MY, HOW TERRIBLE! ONLY *I CAN'T HELP YOU! NOW PLEASE GO!* [*He falls back into his chair, exhausted.*]

WOMAN. [*Crosses to where his foot is resting.*] I'm sorry, Excellency. I hope I haven't caused you any pain.

150 **KISTUNOV.** [*Trying to stop her.*] Please, don't kiss my foot. [*He is too late—she has given his foot a most **ardent** embrace. He screams in pain.*] Aggghhh! Can't you get this into your balding head? If you would just realize that to come to us with this kind of claim is as strange as your trying to get a haircut in a 155 butcher shop.

WOMAN. You can't get a haircut in a butcher shop. Why would anyone go to a butcher shop for a haircut? Are you laughing at me?

KISTUNOV. Laughing! I'm lucky I'm breathing....Pochatkin!

160 **WOMAN.** Did I tell you I'm fasting? I haven't eaten in three days. I want to eat, but nothing stays down. I had the same cup of coffee three times today.

KISTUNOV. [*With his last burst of energy, screams.*] *POCHATKIN!*

165 **WOMAN.** I'm skin and bones. I faint at the least **provocation**....Watch. [*She swoons to the floor.*] Did you see? You saw how I just fainted? Eight times a day that happens.

SECOND READ

Analyze Literature
Drama What is the tone of Kistunov's dialogue here? How can you tell?

ar·dent (är´ dənt) *adj.*, warmth of feeling characterized by eager support

prov·o·ca·tion (präv´ ə kā´ shən) *n.*, something that calls forth an action or emotion

8. **apoplectic.** Bursting with anger

The Assistant *finally rushes in.*

Assistant. What is it, Mr. Kistunov? What's wrong?

170 **Kistunov.** [*Screams.*] GET HER OUT OF HERE! Who let her in my office?

Assistant. You did, sir. I asked you and you said, "Show her in."

Kistunov. I thought you meant a human being, not a lunatic
175 with a doctor's certificate.

Woman. [*To* Pochatkin.] He wouldn't even read it. I gave it to him, he threw it back in my face....You look like a kind person. Have pity on me. You read it and see if my husband is sick or not.

She forces the certificate on Pochatkin.

180 **Assistant.** I *read* it, madame. Twice!

Kistunov. Me too. I had to read it twice too.

Assistant. You just showed it to me outside. You showed it to *everyone.* We *all* read it. Even the doorman.

Woman. You just looked at it. You didn't read it.

185 **Kistunov.** Don't argue. Read it, Pochatkin. For God's sake, read it so we can get her out of here

Assistant. [*Quickly scans it.*] Oh, yes. It says your husband is sick. [*He looks up; gives it to her.*] Now will you please leave, madame, or I will have to get someone to remove you.

190 **Kistunov.** Yes! Yes! Good! Remove her! Get the doorman and two of the guards. Be careful, she's strong as an ox.

Woman. [*To* Kistunov.] If you touch me, I'll scream so loud they'll hear it all over the city. You'll lose all your depositors. No one will come to a bank where they beat weak, defenseless
195 women....I think I'm going to faint again....

Kistunov. [*Rising.*] WEAK? DEFENSELESS? You are as defenseless as a charging rhinoceros! You are as weak as the King of the Jungle![9] You are a plague, madame! A plague that wipes out all that crosses your path! You are a raging river that
200 washes out bridges and stately homes! You are a wind that blows villages over mountains! It is women like you who drive men like me to the condition of husbands like yours!

---

9. King of the Jungle. Lion

WOMAN. Are you saying you're not going to help me?

KISTUNOV. Hit her, Pochatkin! Strike her! I give you
205   permission to knock her down. Beat some sense into her!

WOMAN. [*To* POCHATKIN.] You hear? You hear how I'm
abused? He would have you hit an orphaned mother. Did you
hear me cough? Listen to this cough.

She "racks" up another coughing spell.

ASSISTANT. Madame, if we can discuss this in my office—

He takes her arm.

210   **WOMAN.** Get your hands off me....Help! Help! I'm being
beaten! Oh, merciful God, they're beating me!

ASSISTANT. I am not beating you. I am just holding your arm.

KISTUNOV. Beat her, you fool. Kick her while you've got the
chance. We'll never get her out of here. Knock her senseless!

He tries to kick her, misses and falls to the floor.

215   **WOMAN.** [*Pointing an evil finger at* KISTUNOV, *she jumps on
the desk and punctuates each sentence by stepping on his desk
bell.*] A curse! A curse on your bank! I put on a curse on you
and your depositors! May the money in your vaults turn to
potatoes! May the gold in your cellars turn to onions! May
220   your rubles turn to radishes, and your kopecks to pickles....

KISTUNOV. STOP! Stop it, I beg of you!...Pochatkin, give her
the money. Give her what she wants. Give her anything—only
get her out of here!

WOMAN. [*To* POCHATKIN.] Twenty-four rubles and thirty-six
225   kopecks....Not a penny more. That's all that's due me and that's
all I want.

ASSISTANT. Come with me, I'll get you your money.

WOMAN. And another ruble to get me home. I'd walk but I
have very weak ankles.

230   **KISTUNOV.** Give her enough for a taxi, anything, only get her
out.

WOMAN. God bless you, sir. You're a kind man. I remove the
curse. [*With a gesture.*] Curse be gone! Onions to money,
potatoes to gold—

235   **KISTUNOV.** [*Pulls on his hair.*] REMOVE HERRRR! Oh, God,
my hair is falling out!

He pulls some hair out.

WOMAN. Oh, there's one other thing, sir. I'll need a letter of recommendation so my husband can get another job. Don't bother yourself about it today. I'll be back in the morning. 240 God, bless you, sir....

She leaves.

KISTUNOV. She's coming back....She's coming back....[*He slowly begins to go mad and takes his cane and begins to beat his bandaged leg.*] She's coming back....She's coming back....

Dim-out. ❖

SECOND READ
Analyze Literature
Drama How do the actions indicated in these stage directions help conclude this play?

Mirrors & Windows

When has anyone ever caused you to agree to something unreasonable, just because he or she kept nagging you or making your life unpleasant? Why did you agree? Why might most people act in a similar way?

_____

_____

_____

_____

Find Meaning	Make Judgments
1. (a) What is the setting of the play? (b) In what way is the setting important to the plot?	**4.** (a) What is the overall mood of the play? (b) What details help establish this mood?
2. (a) Why did the Woman come to see Kistunov? (b) Why does Kistunov tell her that she came to the wrong place?	**5.** (a) What are the Woman's most prominent character traits? (b) How do these traits affect her relationship with Kistunov?
3. Why does Kistunov tell his Assistant to give the Woman the money?	**6.** (a) Why did the author call this play "A Defenseless Creature"? (b) What title would you give the play? Why?

Analyze Literature

Drama Reading a drama is different from reading a story. Everything you learn about the setting, characters, and plot is revealed through dialogue spoken by the actors, their actions, or details in the stage directions. Use a chart to analyze how the author uses dialogue and stage directions to create humor in the play.

Dialogue	Stage Directions
	Describe funny actions such as pulling out hair and screaming.

Writing Connection

Informative Writing Write a brief **literary analysis** of "A Defenseless Creature" that focuses on the tone of the play. Begin your analysis with a thesis statement. Use evidence from the play to support your analysis. Describe the effect of the play's tone on the audience.

Folk Literature Close Reading Model

FIRST READING — Key Ideas and Details – What the text says

Build Background

Apply two types of background to read myths, fables, and folk tales effectively. One type is the story's literary and cultural context. The other type of background is the personal knowledge and experience you bring to your reading.

Set Purpose

Folk literature presents characters and actions to say something about life. Set your purpose for reading to decide what you want to get out of the story.

Make Connections

Notice where connections can be made between the story and your life or another story, myth, or legend. What feelings or thoughts do you have while reading the story?

Use reading skills

Use Reading Skills, such as identifying the main idea, analyzing cause and effect, and making inferences, to help you get the most out of your reading. Identify a graphic organizer to help you apply the skill before and while you read.

SECOND READING — Craft and Structure – How the text says it

Use Text Organization

- Break the text down or "chunk" the text into smaller sections to check your comprehension.
- Stop at the end of paragraphs or sections to summarize what you have read. Reread any difficult parts.

Analyze Literature

Folk literature includes literary techniques, such as plot and setting, to create meaning. What literary elements stand out? Are the characters vivid and interesting? Is there a lesson or moral? As you read, consider how these elements affect your enjoyment and understanding of the story.

Unpack Language

What is the effect of the author's vocabulary and the language choices he or she makes? Make sure to use margin definitions, footnotes, and context clues that give hints to the meaning.

THIRD READING — Integration of Knowledge and Ideas – What the text means

Find Meaning

Reread to recall the important details of the story, such as the sequence of events and character traits. Use this information to help interpret, or explain, the meaning of the story.

Make Judgments

- Analyze the text by examining details and deciding what they contribute to the meaning.
- Evaluate the text by making judgments about how the author creates meaning.

Analyze Literature

Review how the use of literary elements increases your understanding of the story. For example, if the story includes dialogue, how does it help shape the story's meaning?

Extend Understanding

Go beyond the text by exploring the story through writing or other creative projects.

Persephone and Demeter page 501

GREEK MYTH retold by Ingri and Edgar Parin d'Aulaire

Build Background

Cultural Context As long as nine thousand years ago, civilizations existed in the lands around the Aegean Sea, in present-day Greece and Turkey. Architecture and arts such as sculpture, pottery, and music flourished in these societies. The literature of that time was passed on by word of mouth, and many stories were told about the Greek pantheon of gods and goddesses.

Reader's Context Think about your own relationships. What friend or family member cheers you up? What qualities make that person so special?

_____

_____

Analyze Literature

Myth A traditional story that usually presents supernatural events involving gods and heroes is called a **myth.** There are many different kinds of myths. An *origin myth,* like "Persephone and Demeter," is a story that explains the existence of things or events in the natural world. As you read "Persephone and Demeter," determine what real-world phenomena it explains.

Set Purpose

Preview the vocabulary words and footnotes. Then skim for other unfamiliar words and look them up.

Use Reading Skills

Monitor Comprehension One good method for monitoring your comprehension is to pose questions about the text. As you read, ask yourself: What have I learned about Greek myth? To what characters, events, settings, and ideas have I been introduced? Use a K-W-L chart to record your ideas.

What I Know	What I Want to Know	What I Learned
Persephone and Demeter were Greek goddesses.		

A Greek Myth retold by Ingri and Edgar Parin D'Aulaire

Persephone and Demeter

1 Persephone grew up on Olympus[1] and her gay laughter rang through the brilliant halls. She was the daughter of Demeter, goddess of the harvest, and her mother loved her so dearly she could not bear to have her out of her sight. When Demeter sat on her golden throne her daughter was always on her lap; when she went down to earth to look after her trees and fields, she took Persephone. Wherever Persephone danced on her light feet, flowers sprang up. She was so lovely and full of grace that even Hades,[2] who saw so little, noticed her and fell in love with her. He wanted her for his queen, but he knew that her mother would never consent to part with her, so he decided to carry her off.

2 One day as Persephone ran about in the meadow gathering flowers, she strayed away from her mother and the attending nymphs.[3] Suddenly, the ground split open and up from the **yawning** crevice came a dark chariot drawn by black horses. At the reins stood grim Hades. He seized the terrified girl, turned his horses, and plunged back into the ground. A herd of pigs **rooting** in the meadow tumbled into the **cleft**, and Persephone's cries for help died out as the ground closed again as suddenly as it had opened. Up in the field, a little swineherd[4] stood and wept over the pigs he had lost, while Demeter rushed wildly about in the meadow, looking in vain for her daughter, who had vanished without leaving a trace.

3 With the frightened girl in his arms, Hades raced his snorting horses down away from the sunlit world. Down and down they sped on the dark path to his dismal underground palace. He led weeping Persephone in, seated her beside him on a throne of black marble, and decked her with gold and precious stones. But the jewels brought her no joy. She wanted no cold stones. She longed for warm sunshine and flowers and

FIRST READ

Use Reading Skills
Monitor Comprehension Why does Hades decide to kidnap Persephone?

yawn•ing (yô´ niŋ) *adj.,* wide open

root (rüt) *v.,* dig in the ground
cleft (kleft) *n.,* space made when something breaks open

---

1. **Olympus.** Mountain in what is now Thessaly, Greece, where the ancient Greeks believed most gods lived
2. **Hades.** God of the underworld; sometimes the name *Hades* is used for the underworld itself
3. **nymphs.** Minor female goddesses who live in natural spots like forests or trees, rivers, and streams
4. **swineherd.** Person who keeps or tends pigs

FIRST READ

Make Connections How does Persephone feel about Hades's riches? How would you feel if you were in her place?

a•veng•ing (ə venj´ iŋ) *adj.*, taking revenge or punishing someone for something

bar•ren (ber´ ən) *adj.*, unable to reproduce or bear fruit; desolate

FIRST READ

Use Reading Skills
Monitor Cmprehension Why does Demeter's grief have an effect on nature?

FIRST READ

Use Reading Skills
Monitor Comprehension How does Demeter find out what happened to Persephone?

her golden-tressed[5] mother.

4   Dead souls crowded out from cracks and crevices to look at their new queen, while ever more souls came across the Styx[6] and Persephone watched them drink from a spring under dark poplars. It was the spring of Lethe[7] and those who drank from its waters forgot who they were and what they had done on earth. Rhadamanthus, a judge of the dead, dealt out punishment to the souls of great sinners. They were sentenced to suffer forever under the whips of the **avenging** Erinyes.[8] Heroes were led to the Elysian fields,[9] where they lived happily forever in never-failing light.

5   Around the palace of Hades there was a garden where whispering poplars and weeping willows grew. They had no flowers and bore no fruit and no birds sang in their branches. There was only one tree in the whole realm of Hades that bore fruit. That was a little pomegranate[10] tree. The gardener of the underworld offered the tempting pomegranates to the queen, but Persephone refused to touch the food of the dead.

6   Wordlessly she walked through the garden at silent Hades' side and slowly her heart turned to ice.

7   Above, on earth, Demeter ran about searching for her lost daughter, and all nature grieved with her. Flowers wilted, trees lost their leaves, and the fields grew **barren** and cold. In vain did the plow cut through the icy ground; nothing could sprout and nothing could grow while the goddess of the harvest wept. People and animals starved and the gods begged Demeter again to bless the earth. But she refused to let anything grow until she had found her daughter.

8   Bent with grief, Demeter turned into a gray old woman. She returned to the meadow where Persephone had vanished and asked the sun if he had seen what had happened, but he said no, dark clouds had hidden his face that day. She wandered around the meadow and after a while she met a youth whose name was Triptolemus. He

---

5. **golden-tressed.** Having golden hair (tresses); blond
6. **Styx.** Main river of the underworld, which surrounds it and separates it from the world of the living
7. **Lethe.** River of forgetfulness
8. **Erinyes.** Three spirits of punishment
9. **Elysian fields.** Paradise
10. **pomegranate.** Round, red fruit with a hard rind

told her that his brother, a swineherd, had seen his pigs disappear into the ground and had heard the frightened screams of a girl.

9   Demeter now understood that Hades had kidnapped her daughter, and her grief turned to anger. She called to Zeus[11] and said that she would never again make the earth green if he did not command Hades to return Persephone. Zeus could not let the world perish and he sent Hermes[12] down to Hades, bidding him to let Persephone go. Even Hades had to obey the orders of Zeus, and sadly he said farewell to his queen.

10   Joyfully, Persephone leaped to her feet, but as she was leaving with Hermes, a hooting laugh came from the garden. There stood the gardener of Hades, grinning. He pointed to a pomegranate from which a few of the kernels were missing. Persephone, lost in thought, had eaten the seeds, he said.

11   Then dark Hades smiled. He watched Hermes lead Persephone up to the bright world above. He knew that she must return to him, for she had tasted the food of the dead.

12   When Persephone again appeared on earth, Demeter sprang to her feet with a cry of joy and rushed to greet her daughter. No longer was she a sad old woman, but a **radiant** goddess. Again she blessed her fields and the flowers bloomed anew and the grain ripened.

ra·di·ant (rā′ dē ənt) *adj.*, shining bright

13   "Dear child," she said, "never again shall we be parted. Together we shall make all nature bloom." But joy soon was changed to sadness, for Persephone had to admit that she had tasted the food of the dead and must return to Hades. However, Zeus decided that mother and daughter should not be parted forever. He ruled that Persephone had to return to Hades and spend one month in the underworld for each seed she had eaten.

14   Every year, when Persephone left her, Demeter grieved, nothing grew, and there was winter on earth. But as soon as her daughter's light footsteps were heard, the whole earth burst into bloom. Spring had come. As long as mother and daughter were together, the earth was warm and bore fruit.

15   Demeter was a kind goddess. She did not want mankind to starve during the cold months of winter when Persephone was away. She lent her chariot, laden with grain, to Triptolemus,

SECOND READ

Analyze Literature
Myth What is one natural phenomenon this myth attempts to explain?

---

11. **Zeus.** King of the Greek gods
12. **Hermes.** Messenger god

the youth who had helped her to find her lost daughter. She told him to scatter her golden grain over the world and teach men how to sow it in spring and reap it in fall and store it away for the long months when again the earth was barren and cold. ❖

Mirrors & Windows

When have you, like Demeter, experienced an emotion that changed your outlook on life? Was the emotion positive or negative? In what ways can emotions be both destructive and constructive?

Close Reading

Find Meaning	Make Judgments
1. (a) What is it like in the underworld? (b) How is this different from the world above?	**4.** What do you think Hades's decision to kidnap Persephone says about his personality?
2. According to the myth, what happens to great sinners after they die? To heroes?	**5.** (a) Does Persephone's schedule at the end of the story seem fair to you? (b) How would you have settled the problem if you were Zeus?
3. (a) How does Demeter react when Persephone is kidnapped? (b) In what ways is this similar to how a human mother would react?	

Analyze Literature

Myth What aspects of the natural world and human experience are explained in the myth "Persephone and Demeter"? Create a two-column chart to document your ideas. In the first column, write the questions people might have had about their world, and in the second, write the details from the story that help to answer those questions.

Real-world Question	Myth's Explanation
What makes plants grow?	

Writing Connection

Argumentative Writing In "Persephone and Demeter," the goddess Demeter must appeal to Zeus to help save her daughter. Put yourself in Demeter's place and write a short **persuasive speech** to deliver to Zeus. A successful persuasive argument begins with a statement of the writer's position, followed by three or more reasons supporting that position.

Eshu page 507

YORUBAN FOLK TALE retold by Judith Gleason

Build Background

Cultural Context The Yoruba people live primarily in southwestern Nigeria, an area they settled about a thousand years ago. According to Yoruban tradition, Earth and heavens were created by a supreme being, Oludumare. Below him were several hundred minor deities, or Orisha, and among the most powerful of those was Eshu. He was not only a trickster—a traditional figure of mischief—but also the messenger who carried news from Earth to Oludumare.

Reader's Context When has a foolish argument threatened one of your friendships? How did you resolve the situation?

Analyze Literature

Folk Tale Stories passed by word of mouth from generation to generation are **folk tales.** They often depict everyday activities and the adventures of common people. In addition, folk tales sometimes include gods and other supernatural characters. As you read, think about how "Eshu" depicts daily life in this community.

Set Purpose

Preview "Eshu," looking for unfamiliar terms. Write down any words and phrases you would like to investigate further.

Use Reading Skills

Identify the Main Idea The main idea, or theme, is what the author wants you to know or think after reading a work. The main idea is often not stated outright. Readers need to examine supporting details of the dialogue, tone, description, plot, and characterization to identify the main idea. Create a main idea map to help you determine the main idea of "Eshu."

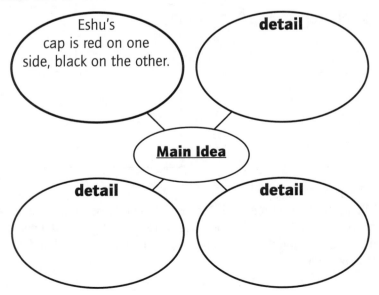

Eshu's cap is red on one side, black on the other.

detail

Main Idea

detail

detail

A Yoruban Folk Tale retold by Judith Gleason

Eshu

1   There were two friends who loved each other like yam porridge and pepper soup. Whenever they went out, they wore identical cloths. Their farm plots, thanks to the chief's respect for their friendship, were adjoining. The path to and from the village was all that divided them as they worked, and all day long they called across **courteous** greetings:

2   "Good-day my very special friend, I hope the sun is not beating too hard upon your shoulders."

3   "Not at all, my dear age-mate; I salute you for working so steadily in the heat."

4   "May your soil yield even finer crops than mine."

5   "My compliments upon your new wife; may she bring forth sons to commend your industry."

6   "Salutations on the coming cool of the evening."

7   "May the sun not deceive you into lingering too late in the field."

8   And so on, as weaver bird[1] converses with weaver bird, these friends continued to embroider their amity.[2]

9   Until one day an old man walked down the path between them. It was Eshu. He was wearing a pointed cap, black on one side and red on the other. He held his pipe to the nape of his neck[3] and slung his stick over his shoulder so that it dangled down his back instead of over his chest as he usually carried it. The two friends answered his greeting, then went on with their work and thought no more about him until, late in the afternoon as they prepared to go home, one of them said, "I wonder what business that old man had in our village?"

10   "Whatever it was, he must have completed it quickly," said the other.

11   "How do you know?"

12   "Because he left before noon, don't you remember? Long before our wives brought out our dinners."

13   "True, he passed by midmorning," said the other, "but he was heading into the village, not out of it."

---

1. weaver bird. Type of bird known for being very social and for making elaborate hanging nests by interweaving grasses and other fibers
2. embroider their amity. Increase their friendship
3. nape of his neck. Back of his neck

FIRST READ
Use Reading Skills
Visualize Picture the two friends' work plots. How are they arranged?

cour•te•ous (kʉr´ tē əs) *adj.,* polite; well mannered

SECOND READ
Analyze Literature
Folk Tale What have you learned so far about daily life in this setting?

14   "Nonsense," said his friend, "he was going in the opposite direction, up country, not towards the village as you said. Perhaps you've confused him with another. This traveler was an old, old man with a stick slung over his shoulder. You know, the one who used to wear a black cap."

15   "Don't take that tone with me. I know precisely who he is, and today he looked exactly the same and, as always, his face was following his pipe bowl into our village."

16   "You looked at his pipe, but I saw his feet. For all we know, he may have been puffing through a hole in the back of his neck; but this much is clear: That old man in his brand new red hat was leaving our village farther and farther behind him."

17   "How absurd to talk about backwards pipe-smoking. You're just trying to throw me off the track."

18   "Not at all. There are infinite possibilities in this world, which only a clod like you would fail to consider. For example, it's perfectly possible, although unlikely, that the sun won't set this evening. What I saw I saw, without error, and you, too stubborn to admit your lack of observation, your lack of imagination, **retaliate** by accusing me of playing with the facts just to get a wedge under your bulk. Why shouldn't a man buy a hat of a different color? And why shouldn't he invent a new way of smoking? I've half a mind to cut a hole in the back of my neck just to show you it can be done."

19   "And stop the sun, I suppose. I've always thought you a little mad, and now I'm convinced of it. Some witch is eating you. You ought to go to a doctor—"

20   "So that's it! I don't care what you think. You're impossible. I can't imagine why I ever found you good company. Your stupid face revolts me. I can't stop myself," he said, hitting his friend over the head with his hoe.

21   "So you admit you're mad, mad enough to pick a fight with me. Well I accept the challenge. Crazy or not, there's but one way to deal with unreasonable aggressors." And with that he threw his one-time friend flat on his back.

22   "Crude, evil-tempered man," said the other, "flat-footed rhinoceros, illegitimate offspring of a mortar and pestle.[4] Begone. I don't care how late it is. I wouldn't walk home at midnight with you. Our friendship is finished. Dead. No words will ever pass between us again."

---

4. **mortar and pestle.** Device for pulverizing herbs

re·tal·i·ate (ri ta´ lē āt') *v.*, respond to an action by doing a similar thing back, usually in a negative sense, such as repaying one injury by inflicting another

FIRST READ

Use Reading Skills
Identify the Main Idea What does this friend's claim that he always thought the other was "a little mad" suggest about the main idea?

23　　When the chief heard of the **astonishing** quarrel between these two whose loyalty he had always supposed more durable than that of other men, he sighed deeply and went off to perform a sacrifice to Eshu. The next time village council met, he reallocated[5] the land so that henceforth the former friends would work at opposite corners of the communal tract. Then, holding up an old hoe for all to see, he said, mysteriously, "The sacrifice that iron refused to make is what's eating him." ❖

5. **reallocated.** Reassigned

as•ton•ish•ing (ə stä´ ni shiŋ) *adj.*, amazing; very surprising

FIRST READ

Use Reading Skills
Make Inferences What does the chief's response to the quarrel tell you about his character?

Mirrors & Windows

Think of a time when you had a quarrel with a close friend or family member. What caused this conflict? Why are some friendships stronger than others?

_____

_____

_____

_____

Find Meaning	Make Judgments
1. (a) How exactly does Eshu trick the two friends? (b) What does his success suggest about their friendship?	**3 .** Why do you think Eshu acts the way he does?
2. What does the chief say at the end of the tale?	**4.** (a) Which parts of the folk tale do you find funny? (b) How might humor help convey the main idea?

Analyze Literature

Folk Tale Folk tales often depict everyday activities and the adventures of common people. These stories offer insights into the culture from which they come. What have you learned about Yoruban culture and everyday life from this folk tale? Create a list of details from the folk tale that help paint a picture of Yoruban culture. Then write a sentence that summarizes what you know.

Yoruban Culture
1. Agricultural community
2.
3.
My Summary:

Writing Connection

Informative Writing Can you think of a better solution than the one the chief devised? Write a brief **critical analysis** about the problem solving that occurs in "Eshu." Begin by stating your opinion of the chief's actions. Then briefly describe and discuss the problems the characters face and suggest your own solutions.